What people are saying about Eternally at War . . .

"Every human being needs to have their life validated. Medals and assumptions of honorable conduct vaporize in a world of contempt for Captain Robert Lathrop. The degeneration of his thought process, as he moves through the doctors drug culture, make PTSD even more debilitating.

Jeanette Vaughan writes a very moving literary description of a pilot who cannot come home. Her empathy makes us feel that Gene and Jeanette actively collaborated with each other. They reach out to us from their newly found universe. Very interesting presentation of PTSD, must read."
-- Ann Miles,Ph.D. Executive Director, Carriage Barn Adaptive Therapy Program, Kensington, NH,
http://www.carriage-barn.org

"A fantastic read! A gripping and emotional story of a heroic Marine combat pilot and a very troubled man. It opened up my Vietnam memory locker. I always felt that if you were not there, you could not understand."
-- Lt. Col Bob Trumpfheller, USMC (Ret), VMA-311, A-4
   pilot

"This work is invaluable for many reasons but especially for preserving the history of the Vietnam War and, in the process of doing so, honoring those who served."
-- Dr. Richard Verrone, Ph.D. previous Director of the Oral History Project, Texas Tech University Vietnam Center and Archive

"A page-turning brilliant read that honors our veterans."
-- Corporal Jim Galchick, USMC, VMA-311 1968
   President of VMA-311 Reunion Association

"War is hell. For many of the U.S. veterans who served in the Vietnam Conflict, the psychological nightmare rages on even 40 years after the last Marines left Siagon. This is an important read."
-- Brian Handwerk, *The Smithsonian Magazine*

"A great book on the air war and how it affected this pilot."
-- Captain Bob Miecznikowski, USMC (Ret), VMA-211, A-4 pilot

"I couldn't believe how it brought me back to that place and time. So many important memories that I had tried to forget. Thank you, Gene for making me remember."
-- Colonel Ronald Suter, USMC (Ret), VMA-311, A-4 pilot

"I, too, am a Vietnam Veteran living with PTSD and share a similar story. It's a long road back. The journey will take many of us the rest of our lives."
-- Ed Swauger, Author of *Earning the CIB - The Making of a Soldier in Vietnam*

"Married to a Vietnam Veteran also diagnosed with PTSD, I know firsthand how debilitating living with this diagnosis can be. Kudos to Captain Lathrop for fighting his way back from a place no one should ever have been."
-- Laine Raia, Author/Editor and proprietor of *The Ponderaia*, www.ponderaia.com North Reading, MA

"War is the most expensive dispute resolution method known to man. In war, everyone pays a price; both winners and losers equally. That price can be calculated in terms of lives lost as well as in lives destroyed. Captain Robert Lathrop proudly served his nation in Vietnam. *Eternally at War* shares insights into PTSD long before there was a name for it. Long before effective treatment was available. This book is a must read for anyone working with or living with someone who has PTSD."
--Bonnie Marlewski-Probert, author, founder of Whitehall PR http://whitehallpr.com

Also by Jeanette Vaughan

Flying Solo
Solo Vietnam
Waiting in the Wings

Also by Captain Robert Lathrop
and Jeanette Vaughan

The Dark Side of Heaven

Eternally at War

Captain Robert "Gene" Lathrop, USMC

and

Jeanette Vaughan

AgeView Press

Blue Ridge, TX MMXVI

All main characters appearing in this work served their country with honor. Those that died, did so with honor. Any resemblance to real persons is with their consent. Other names have been changed to protect their privacy.

Cover photo credit: C.L. Stegall
http://www.clstegall.com

DEDICATION

This book was written to honor the extraordinary men and women who serve in our U.S. Armed Forces, most endearingly to those who served during the Vietnam War. God bless those who safely returned home, at times suffering the aftermath of war for years and especially those who didn't.

ACKNOWLEDGMENTS

The Vietnam War has always fascinated me. I remember as a young girl donning a copper POW bracelet. I wore it proudly and prayed every day that the brave man taken prisoner made it home. It was an honor to interview the men and women who helped make this book a reality. Pilots, nurses and infantry gave texture to the sights and sounds of a foreign land. I am especially grateful to the pilots willing to share their stories. It was a time that was difficult and very misunderstood. For some, excruciatingly painful to remember.

First off I would like to acknowledge Captain Robert Lathrop, USMC, RIP. The many missions in this book were based on his manuscripts which he wrote as therapy and which are now housed in the Texas Tech University Vietnam Center and Archive. Also, many thanks to the historians such as Dr. Richard Verrone and his graduate students who recorded the oral histories of many veterans sessions preserving them for history. The center is home to a vast collection of dialogues, photographs, and written documents giving vivid insight to a chaotic war.

I would also like to acknowledge several USMC pilots, officers and enlisted who have become my friends and colleagues. The pilots of VMA-311 and their aviation crews, especially Captain Peter Erenfeld. Peter provided an insight to the effects that war had on Gene. Both good and bad. But never let go of his allegiance to his wingman and friend.

Finally, I would like to thank Joy Lathrop. Her willingness to be vulnerable in releasing Gene's works to me as an author was invaluable. She wishes nothing more than to bring attention to the post-war dilemma that still faces so many of our young men and women who have served courageously in active war atrocities, creating what we now know as the plague of PTSD. Her hope is that through Gene's experiences, others will recognize the effects of PTSD and seek treatment.

I am humbled and forever grateful for all of my military colleagues' time, attention to detail and generous lend of their materials and literary works. As Americans we should forever be indebted to their bravery and service.

Eternally at War

Map of Vietnam

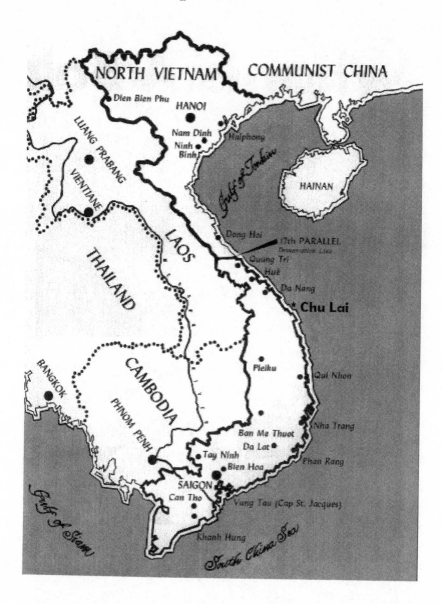

FOREWORD

War is not a natural act for humans. Yet, we have been killing each other since Cain slew Able. Any civilized person who has been in combat, seen his friends killed, been shot at and killed people has experienced an event that will forever affect their lives. It is unfortunate but it is the warriors who pay the ultimate price when our nation participates in any war.

PTSD was not recognized by the Veterans Administration until the early 1980's. Accordingly, the government's position was, "it didn't exist."

The Vietnam war produced more people with PTSD than any previous war in which the United States participated. There are several reasons for this. World War II veterans went to war as a unit and for the most part returned home as a unit. They were hailed as conquering heroes upon their return, which in my opinion they are. They were given parades and returned to good jobs. Many of the combatants suffered from PTSD which at that time was called, "shell shock." They were not treated for this condition. It wasn't until after the Vietnam War that WWII and Korean War veterans came forward and were treated for PTSD. Today, veterans of the Gulf War, Iraq War and Afghanistan War have treatment for PTSD available to them for the asking.

Both World War II and the Korean War had a strategy for victory. The Vietnam War was different from previous wars in that there was no strategy for victory. There was no unit cohesion. You went to war as an individual and were assigned to a unit after you arrived in Vietnam. When your twelve or thirteen-month tour was over, you returned to the U.S. as an individual and did your best to return to civilian life. Vietnam veterans did not come home to a grateful nation. They were treated like pariahs in their own country, spat upon and called, "baby killers." For these veterans, life would never be the same.

The Vietnam War was fought as a war of attrition. Body count was the measurement as to whether we won or lost a battle. In 1967 Lyndon Johnson said, "I will not send American boys to do what Vietnamese boys should be doing for themselves." Well, he lied. In 1968 there were more than 500,000 American troops in Vietnam. Battles were fought and targets bombed by Marine, Navy and Air force pilots only after the President and the Secretary of Defense approved the targets. The Military Assistance Command Vietnam (MACV) sent a request to Washington to bomb certain targets. That request went from Vietnam to Hawaii to Washington and back the same way. This allowed the enemy to eavesdrop on these approved targets and to know exactly where our planes would strike.

The enemy would, by then, have reinforced the target areas with Anti-Aircraft fire and SAM missiles which resulted in thousands of our planes being shot down. Politics was the reason the U.S. did not win the war. The Generals, who should have run the war, were hamstrung by our Commander in Chief. This resulted in the tragic loss of life and imprisonment for many of our pilots who flew over North Vietnam. No other war, in which the U.S. had participated, could match the political mess of the Vietnam War. The press corps were also responsible for America abandoning the Vietnamese as well as the politicians.

The year 1968 was a massive turning point in the war. It was the year of the TET Offensive. Every large base in Vietnam was attacked by the North Vietnamese and the Viet Cong. In spite of what was reported on the news, TET was an unmitigated disaster for the enemy. By June of 1968, the Viet Cong were virtually destroyed and the North Vietnamese suffered extensive defeats throughout South Vietnam. For all practical purposes, we were winning the war. Then disaster struck. President Lyndon Johnson stopped the bombing of North Vietnam in an effort to boost Hubert Humphrey's run for the White House and to get the North Vietnamese to return to the peace talks. Within ten days, the North Vietnam roads were crammed with trucks hauling supplies down the Ho Chi Min trail. At night, pilots who flew up to the Demilitarized Zone, saw streams of headlights as trucks brought supplies to that area. General Giap, the head of the North Vietnam military, wrote in his memoirs that had we continued bombing the north, they would have in all probability negotiated a peace settlement. However, this was not to be, all because of the politics of Washington.

This biography of Captain Robert (Gene) Lathrop is the story of a "Gung Ho" Marine Pilot, whether he believed he was or not and how the Vietnam war affected him. Flying in an extremely hostile environment, the missions he flew were either Close Air Support, Radar Controlled Bombing or the Hot Pad. The Close Air Support mission was generally a bombing mission in support of ground troops. Radar controlled bombing missions were flown at night as single plane missions. These missions were either in South Vietnam, Laos or North Vietnam. Hot pad missions required the pilot to be airborne within five minutes to support a ground unit in trouble.

Captain Lathrop's reaction to his missions was unique in that he viewed them very intensely. By constantly replaying the missions in his mind, he became overly sensitive to each sortie and was haunted by memories of these events. He was not the only pilot who had problems. Some pilots did not want to fly, others relished it and others flew with a ho hum complacent attitude.

By the time he completed his thirteen-month tour in Vietnam, he went home with many questions regarding his missions. Gene had a degree in Forestry Management from the University of Idaho. When he left the Marine Corps he went to work in the forests of southern Oregon. Gene spent many months working alone in the forests and as a result had ample time to reflect on Vietnam. By then the war was not going well and almost every-one knew it was hopeless. The "get out of Vietnam riots" in our country were difficult for veterans to accept as many believed their friends were killed for naught. Veterans who were able to find jobs among friends and co-workers adjusted much easier to civilian life than those working alone. Many vets turned to alcohol and drugs to mask the flashbacks and intrusive thoughts about the war. Marriages failed, work became intolerable and "fitting in" eluded many veterans.

Gradually, veterans began to seek treatment at VA hospitals, at the urging of wives and loved ones. Unfortunately for Gene, the damage was done by months of job-related isolation and the re-playing of old war tapes in his mind. His story is not about a weak person. This is a tale of a warrior and great pilot who was laid low by circumstances beyond his control, beyond his understanding and even beyond the understanding of the government. It would be many years before the government truly understood the effects of PTSD on the young men and women who served.

In reading this biography, you will get a sense of his desperation and driving need for answers. The effects of all the medications he was required to take to treat the PTSD might have skewed some of his memories. Allow his story to be told without picking apart the details. This is a journal all veterans should read because we now face an identical situation with Iraq and Afghanistan veterans. Fortunately, our country now reacts to war veterans with a "welcome home" attitude and the recognition and ability to treat those with PTSD.

To Gene Lathrop, I say, "Rest in Peace", you were a great pilot and friend.

Captain Peter Erenfeld, USMC, VMA-311

Prologue

∞ September, 1944 Walla Walla, WA ∞

War is hell. I have an image. Fire. Burning. Acrid
smells of an explosion of petroleum. It has been
permanently etched into the synapses of my mind.
As far back as I can remember anything at all. Way before I
experienced the atrocities of war, I had my first traumatic
experience. According to the newspaper article I found forty-
five years later, I was just over two years old when this real
nightmare occurred.

It was during the first weeks of September. My father had
come home after work in his beat-up, old pickup with the
cracked windshield and beckoned my mother outside.

"Hurry, up! There's a commotion going on at the edge of
town. Get your shoes on and get out to the truck."

We all ran out to the pickup, me in the arms of my mother.
Driving in the dark through the city streets of Walla Walla we
headed up towards the Blue Mountains near Wenatchee. The
image seared on my mind was formed as we parked there. I was
standing on the seat. At first, my mother let out a shriek of
horror and put her head down, not wanting to look. Then she

started crying as my father got out of the pickup and strode into the darkness.

Despite standing on the front seat next to her, I was not as tall as my seated mother. A powerful feeling I could not understand came over me. It must have been fear. Because fear, I came to know in later years, burned images into my mind.

Behind us, a Chrysler with bright orange fenders and a light brown hood was parked with the lights off. Perhaps only thirty yards behind us, the car was lit up so that you could see it nearly as plain as if it were daylight. Reflections of flames flickered on its hood. Flames from a large object on fire close by. A group of men, heads down, were wearing pullover jackets and standing equidistant from each other. Some held their fedora hats over their eyes. Their backs to the field, some looked over their shoulders at what was behind them.

In front of us, not well lit up, was a gray Chevrolet coupe, the panels dull in the darkness. No one was between our pickup and the Chevy ahead. There were more men, though, standing along the road, their hands in their pockets, also spaced apart from one another. No one was talking. There was only silence.

I peered out the cracked front window, straining to see beyond my sobbing mother. Nothing. Then, I looked over my mother's shoulder, her head still down, out the back. I pushed against the shoulder pads in her light coat and tried to see out the side window. My mother was young, maybe twenty-two or three at the time. Her red hair was squared off pageboy style. A bandana was tied gracefully on her still bowed head.

Through the side window, spreading from horizon to horizon and as high as I could see, was a wall of flames. Roaring. Beating upward toward the dark heavens. Perhaps only a couple hundred yards away. The orange and yellow fire roared and rolled, ripping at the night sky. Covering the entire vantage point, the flames lit up the field and the silhouettes of the men silently standing watch.

None of them moved. They stood smoking, none seeming to recognize the other's existence. An acrid smell filled the air. One that I could not identify at the time. It hung on the upholstery of the pickup. Each time I rode in that truck, from that time on, I could smell the same sickening odor, reminding me of the fire and the images that I didn't like to remember.

The Army had a base in Walla Walla. Large heavy B-17 and B-24 bombers flew in an out constantly, their engines roaring through the sky. Tonight, a B-17 had crashed due to mechanical failure killing five members of the crew onboard. The smell was avaition fuel igniting large plumes of flame and burning all the bodies.

Another image is tied to the flames. There was a large Army evacuation hospital on the west side of town. It used to be an old cavalry fort. There were barracks in which the whole end opened up. When we drove by in the spring, summer and early fall, the doors to the end of the buildings would be open. I could see the men in white strung up in their beds throughout the expansive wards. Pulleys and cords hoisting up their damaged or partially missing limbs.

Other men in white were sitting on the grass near the buildings, smoking, or reading. There was a big fence around it with guard dogs, soldiers and guards. None of the men were smiling. I didn't know it at the time, but they were veterans of war. I remember being terrified every time we drove by that scary place.

We had to pass by the hospital on the way to Touchet, another town some twenty miles way. Since my grandmother and most of my mother's family lived there, we went by the hospital many, many times. I would dive down in the seat rather than look out on all the sadness.

For as far back as I can remember, I was haunted by those scenes. They were the first images that were permanently etched on the soul of my young life. Flames. Fire. Metal disintegrating.

Burning flesh. They were of war, though I didn't know it then. They were of death, but I didn't know that either. The images have always been there. They remain there as clear as they were when I first saw them. The sights, the smells, the sounds that coupled with my experiences in Vietnam kept me eternally at war.

Chapter 1

∞ March 19, 1967 Kingsville, TX ∞

Despite having a background in forestry, not aviation, I had no anxiety training as a Naval flight student. For as long as I can remember, I wanted to be a pilot. As a young boy, I read about the Flying Tigers, which were the 1st American Volunteer Group of the Chinese Air Force. They trained around 1941 or 1942 as a group of nicknamed pilots from the United States Army Air Corps, Navy and Marine Corps.

The group first saw combat twelve days after Pearl Harbor. I remember hearing about their innovative tactical victories on the news, when all the other news in the U.S. was filled with little more than stories of defeat at the hands of the Japanese. But reports of these combat missions and the bravery gave me hope. I saw good in what they were doing and was inspired by their stories that America might defeat our enemies in World War II. Who couldn't remember the shark-faced nose art complete with shark's teeth painted on their planes?

Now, as a First Lieutenant in the United States Marine Corps, I was flying my first tactical bombing training mission. Fearlessly taking to the skies, I flew number two in a formation of five TF-9J aircraft. The Cougar jets were modeled after the Grumman Panther that had flown during the Korean War.

They were underpowered compared to more modern aircraft, but good training planes. Aircraft with excessive power could easily get inexperienced aviators into trouble. In pilot speak, you had to fly the plane to stay ahead of it.

It was a Sunday briefing. We were flying seven days a week, from 4:00 AM until midnight, trying to fast track our training to provide much needed replacements for the fleet. I was one of the few Marine students flying because of a national funding problem. Most military aviators were prevented from commencing their training until the beginning of the fiscal year in July. Guess I just got lucky.

Over the last few months, I had mustered up a lot of confidence flying the F9F-8 and looked forward to the tactical bombing hops. It was nicknamed The Cougar. Wanting to check off my ride with a flight instructor, I was keen to join the fleet. I hadn't received my orders yet, but expected to graduate in the next two weeks. They were due any day.

Driving through base housing in the early dawn, I marveled at the sunrise. It was going to be a great day. I just knew it. I loved to fly, despite my anxieties about going into the Marines instead of the Navy. I knew I never quite fit in with the gung ho, hey diddle-diddle up the middle, macho "semper fi" stuff. I was too much of an independent thinker. I processed stuff and thought things out.

Don't get me wrong, the training you got in the Marine Corps was superb, not only for military endeavors, but for the rest of your life. When they tell you to do something, you don't say, 'I'm not going to do it,' you analyze how you're going to do it and make a decision and do it. They pretty much beat you down to get you to understand that you never give up. Never. Taking action just comes naturally. That kind of decisiveness doesn't always fit in your life later on, but it is a type of training that gives you strength, for officers anyway.

Basic and officer candidate school started at daybreak. We got into formation and marched to breakfast. Marched back. All day we fought with bayonets and rifles. Constantly marching. We ran and climbed hills. And then attended classes. I remember being so very tired. But God forbid if you couldn't keep your eyes open in class. There would be hell to pay.

All the yelling and the drilling. Well, it was tough, but it taught you to follow orders. Discipline in the Marine Corps was just that way. You developed stamina. Whether you were running, or doing pull ups or swimming. Luckily, I had always been an outdoor type as a young man, so I didn't have trouble with the stamina required. You figured out pretty quick that the Marine Corps didn't end at midnight. There were boots to clean and your rifle to muster. Then it was time to do it all over again. Little did I realize, but that training prepared me for future combat missions. Endless missions that started and never seemed to stop.

I just knew the "hey diddle-diddle up the middle whatever stuff" wasn't me. To this day, I rarely am heard to say "Oohrah." Most of the guys I was in training with were young. I was married with a baby. I had fought forest fires and worked as a foreman with the toughest and roughest of people.

As a manager, I had lot more experience in dealing with difficult people than my young Marine counterparts. They were still "gung-ho," "oohrah," naïve and I just wasn't that way. So they perceived me as not being worth a damn. And on top of that, I was a pilot candidate too. Pilots weren't considered real Marines by the infantry. As such, I was in the bottom ten percent at Basic School. But four months later, when back in my element, I was number two in my class in pre-flights.

So today was going to be fine. I was flying with Navy Training Squadron 21, which had a World War II hangar on the east end of the field. The airstrip was located five miles from the Gulf of Mexico out on the dry Texas coastal plains near the immense King Ranch, which extended nearly one hundred miles to the south.

In the ready room, six students and two instructors were briefed for the bombing mission. I would be flying with Captain Fred Harshbarger, a Marine who had just begun flying jet aircraft after medical leave. Seems he had an incident in Virginia where he had ejected at low altitude, his chute catching in a tree and snapping him like a whip. Just back on flight status, he would be flying number two with me.

Briefing by Captain Trumpfheller complete, we manned the aircraft, started them up and taxied in line to the take-off end of the east runway. While in the arming area, the lead aircraft aborted the mission, making me take the lead. As he taxied back in front of me, I called the tower for take-off. I motioned the other four aircraft into position up wind of me so they wouldn't get in my jet wash.

Giving the hand signal to run up the engines, I then put my head back down in the cockpit while I checked my own instruments. Since the F9F-8 didn't have an excess of power, it wasn't in one's best interest to have anything wrong that would limit the performance of the aircraft in any way.

With the engine at full throttle, the instruments showing full power, the gunsight and armament switches checked, I visually checked for a thumbs-up from the other aircraft. Nose lowered and at full thrust, I released my brakes and rolled. There was twenty knots of wind right down the runway, so I didn't have to worry about the short length available on these warm spring days. Bumping along until the plane got enough speed to show airspeed, at 6,000 feet I rotated and lifted up.

It was necessary to hold, pulling up the landing gear just a second or two after getting airborne in the lackluster Cougar. I held the flaps until the plane had accelerated to 190 knots and reached 500 feet. Even at that speed, the Cougar would settle slowly downward, losing some altitude before the airspeed picked up enough to give the plane enough lift to start climbing at a normal rate. God love those training planes.

Easing the plane into a gentle climb after liftoff, I glanced periodically at the airspeed and altitude, wanting to pull up my flaps. It was dusty at liftoff and I headed for the small lagoon that led out to the gulf.

Flying so much during the last five months, I was almost more at home in the cockpit than on the ground. I truly loved flying jet aircraft and would have relished the chance to stay in the air twice as much as I was now flying, if given the opportunity.

Suddenly, just as I leaned back to recheck the airspeed, I reached for the flaps. At 140 knots and 400 feet, upon doing so, there was a loud clunk from the aft part of the aircraft. The nose of the plane pitched over rapidly. Jerking back the stick, nothing happened. I had no control of the tail at all.

Peering out the canopy, I saw the ground coming up fast. The plane was pitching forward and I heard the instructor in the back screaming.

"Eject. Eject, for fuck's sake."

Reaching over my head, I pulled the face curtain. Suddenly, everything was silent and seemed to be occurring in slow motion. The pace of the next few occurrences around me seemed to play out in minutes instead of seconds. The seat was above me in the blue sky. It didn't move. It was stationary with the stabilization chute still attached.

Rolling over slowly to my left, I could see the tail of the F9 sticking up out of the waves of flame flowing ahead of it. Similar to waves that hit the shore on a nearly windless day at the ocean, but these waves were made of fire.

I watched the waves for a fraction of a second, then looked up to see if I had a parachute. I didn't. I glanced back at the advancing fire and saw it expanding toward me as I descended and it engulfed me. It appeared as if I was penetrating the face of a small sun.

I must have been knocked out by the impact with the ground for a few seconds. When I regained consciousness, I was on my knees in the middle of the fireball. There was nowhere to run.

Surrounded by the deep orange, roaring flames, I could feel them burning me. My oxygen mask was melting onto my face and the nylon from my G-suit clung to my legs. My watch was burned into my wrist. The noise of the fire was deafening. The deep orange flames rolled around and reached out from all sides. The heat of the loud snapping fire was made more terrifying by the black hissing tendrils of smoke that sizzled off the ends of each ball of flame as it whipped around me.

There was no way to run out. Fire engulfed and totally surrounded me. It was getting hard to breathe. I couldn't determine which way to run to get away from it. Standing amidst the flames, I was getting more and more panicky. In an instant, a dark area appeared at my one o'clock position. Instinctively, I ran toward it and found a canyon between two walls of fire where I could see direction. I stumbled between the two towering faces of fire, perhaps caused by a wind gust. The walls of flame were so high on each side of me that I couldn't see the tops of them. Rolling fireballs emerged out of the walls and engulfed me, raping my side with pain as they extended out and over me as I attempted to escape.

It felt like an eternity that I was in the fire. When I finally ran out onto the burned dessert grass, the flames wouldn't stop and seemed to follow me as I ran. Ready to give up, as I felt my back burning, I turned, raising my arms in defense. The chute that I thought was missing went out, leaving four of five feet of material in shrouds. The remaining parts of the parachute opened as I continued to run from the fire.

Pulling off my melted G-suit and torso harness, I could tell by the color of the skin on my arms that I was badly scorched. Signs and symptoms of shock came over me. I recognized the slowing of time amidst an unreal feeling. My head was getting lighter. The lack of pain I knew was an indication of impending shock and hindered my critical thinking and situational awareness.

As I looked out, I could see another deployed parachute across the burned area. Most of the fire had extinguished itself, but a few patches of grass and some shrubs were still burning among the embers. I could see the outline of Captain Harshbarger in the grass. The fire had burned up to him and gone out. Still in shock and recognizing that he was bent in the wrong places for me to be able to do anything for him, I collapsed the chute so he would not continue to blow downwind and become even more injured, if he was even still alive.

A helicopter from the Naval Air Station came in a few minutes with a doctor aboard.

"Medical one, this is chopper Charlie Frank one thirty. I've got third degree burns at forty percent. Patient unconscious. Compromised airway. Will transport after emergent crich. Over."

"Charlie Frank one thirty. Roger that. Transport to NAS Corpus Christie. Over."

"Sorry, sir. But we only have room for one. The ground ambos will be here soon, I promise," the medic saluted.

Weakly, I raised my arm to return the salute. I was left on my own, since the injuries I had were not as visible, nor as extreme as those of the flight instructor.

A few fellow students still on the ground had come out after seeing the commotion. Stunned, I was talking to another student from my flight class. The ambulance arrived just as my shock was wearing off. After a two minute ride to the Auxiliary

Air Station Dispensary, it was determined that I had more extensive injuries than had initially been thought.

"You in pain, sir?"

"You could say that," I winced as the pain intensified. "Gimme some Morphine?"

"Straight away, sir."

The poke of the needle was welcome and within minutes, I felt the onset of the opioid ebb away the misery. Bandaging me up, they radioed for another ambulance.

"Medical one. We need another ground transport to NAS Corpus. Over."

The one hour ride in the Pontiac ambulance seemed to go on forever. We were headed to the World War II Naval hospital complete with wood frame buildings and long wards for casualties. Because the accident had made the local news and radio stations, the other cars driving near sensed that I was one of the pilots involved. Peering out the window of the ambulance, I could see them stare.

I had no idea how badly I was injured. Burns covered a good part of my body and a piece of the airplane went through my shoulder. I didn't understand at the time why so many people were gawking and staring.

I spent the next thirty days in the hospital at NAS Corpus. Then another three months as a convalescent outpatient. Third degree burns covered my arms and legs. Thankfully only second degree burns to my face. I had fractured several vertebra in my neck and spine and had the wound on my shoulder from one of the flaps. I requested to be kept at NAS Corpus as long as possible. Two other pilots, both Navy Ensigns, had been transferred to the burn center at Wilford Hall in San Antonio. They died of complications from burns similar to the same type I had received. I spoke with others who visited them.

The consensus was that they perished because they had given up. Depressed by the conditions there. I begged to stay at

NAS Corpus. The Navy docs kept me at Corpus, though I don't know if my request had anything to do with their decision. But I was glad. I was determined to live and fly again.

NAS Corpus was used as one of the evacuation facilities from Vietnam. At first, I was immobile for a week. But during my recovery, when I was able to walk, I would pass through some of the wards that had Vietnam casualties in them. I had never seen anything like what I saw there, even later in the war. So much worse than what I had seen at Walla Walla.

Seeing the unmoving blobs of white through the long halls of the ward, I began blocking the images out. They were like the Army hospital at Walla Walla. Too familiar. Too painful.

During my thirty days as a patient, I penned some poems about what I saw there. Scribbling them down on any paper I could find.

A significant change occurred during my hospitalization. I developed claustrophobia, which now happened in any confined place. I'd never had that before. In addition, I was hurt worse than they knew. Hitting the ground without a chute, I had small fractures in my neck and all throughout my back. But I never complained about the pain and numbness that would shoot down my arm. If the flight surgeon knew, I would have been grounded. I was determined to get back to the flight line.

My accident was no isolated incident. Everyone seemed to know of it. It was similar to other accidents. Turns out, the horizontal stabilizer in the tail was faulty and failed causing my plane to go in. It had to be replaced in every F-9 in the entire world. The advanced Naval Training Command of the U.S. Navy was shut down at a very bad time in the war. Everyone got leave. Except those of us who were in hospital.

My orders for overseas came only a few days after being admitted to the hospital. I was going to Vietnam. At the time, I couldn't bring myself to tell my wife. I didn't need to. Because first, I was headed to Yuma, Arizona to begin familiarization training with a squadron flying the A-4 Skyhawk.

Chapter 2

∞ January, 1968 Yuma, AZ ∞

Most of the people I had gone to flight training with had graduated and were now flying in the fleet with the Marines or Navy. Although I had finished flight training in six weeks, I now found myself having to go through some basic flying again. I graduated around the first of September.

Seeing the effects of the war while at Corpus before going to Vietnam on my combat tour had changed my perspective in the cockpit. No longer did I walk with the cocky, arrogant swagger of invincibility. I was more cautious. My sensory awareness was piqued about what could happen. The accident had taken away much of my brashness, if not my confidence. That wasn't good in a fighter pilot.

I had seen the stress lines on the faces and the pained looks in the eyes of other pilots who had been shot down. But I would be damned before I was going to let that happen to me. So, I blocked it out.

After only fifty or so hours flying the two-seat TA-4F, I was transferred to VRF-32, a fixed wing ferry squadron to fly a series of aircraft over to Vietnam. These A-4s were going to be set up as air control aircraft out of Da Nang and were to be used for spotting targets. I was assigned temporarily to Navy

Ferry Squadron 12. The six of us from Yuma were assigned to ferry the six VMT-103 TA-4F two seat aircraft from VMT-103 in order to restock the squadrons. The pilots included two flight instructors, two Marine pilots who would be staying in Vietnam and two students, including myself. We were designated with wings which qualified us as naval aviators.

I was more afraid flying over the ocean in a single engine plane than I ever was in combat. Hours in a small cockpit over nothing but ocean. And the cockpit itself. With me standing over six feet, it was very claustrophobic. Plus, I was flying after a hell of a lot of stress. I went to Vietnam with post-traumatic stress disorder, PTSD. I'm sure of that now.

Twenty-two other Marine and Navy replacement aircraft would be making the journey across the Pacific Ocean with aerial refueling. From Yuma, we flew to El Toro Marine Corps Air Station, near Los Angeles to pick up the rest. Next, we flew about seven hours out to Hawaii. From Kaneohe Bay Marine Corps Air Station, near Honolulu, we flew another seven to Wake Island, then four to Guam, then a little less to the Philippine island in Subic Bay, NAS Cubi Point and finally the two and a half hour leg to Da Nang.

Flying for hours over the navy blue ocean in the tiny cockpit of the A-4 and seeing nothing but water for hours on end is physically and mentally numbing. If even once, you saw something other than water, or heard anything on the radio, or had some reassurance that you were not totally alone – thousands of miles from nowhere, the flying wouldn't be so bad. But the norm was to lapse into boredom for hours on end.

However, when something scary and out of the ordinary shocks you into reality, you only wish that you could return to the boredom.

"Sierra delta zero eight. This is number one. Hate to tell you all this, but I just ran out of oxygen. You all had better check yours. Over."

Shit. We were one third of the way between Wake Island and Guam. Stark terror over took me, after hearing that message. My stomach turned over as I realized that I too, had the same lack of oxygen that the lead did. Fear was replaced by extreme anxiety for two hours until we got clearance and direction to fly at a lower altitude to breathe the cabin air.

Flying at a lower altitude caused the fuel flow to go up. I was continually computing my fuel supply again and again, hoping to make it to target. Meanwhile, the search planes were being launched, just in case.

We finally made it to Guam, on fumes, with little fuel to spare. But only five of us would continue. One of the A-4s froze up on landing. I heard it on the radio.

"Guam tower. This is Sierra Delta one six. Over."

"Go ahead one six."

"I've got a problem. Seems my scooter's all froze up."

"Shit. Roger, that one six. Is your throttle stable?"

"Throttle stable. Over."

"Damned left over Navy pieces of shit. Emergency landing activated. Set her down as easy as you can."

"Yeah. Thanks."

Normally, when a plane freezes up, it's usually when the bearings go out. Turns out the engine had a cracked oil seal. Despite the problem, he landed without much drama. Just another day on the Marine flight line.

After a brief refuel, we flew on to Cubi Point. The color of the water in this part of the world was something to behold. Cobalt blue. Nothing short of spectacular.

Our journey and readiness for take-off was halted, however. Initially, we were held on the runway at Cubi Point because we were being loaded with guns. Apparently, the USS Pueblo, a spy ship, had been attacked by North Korea and was under attack while we prepared for take-off. Despite being loaded with armaments, our services were not needed. Unfortunately, the ship had been captured quickly. Ordnance unloaded, we were then cleared for take-off to Vietnam.

The flight to Da Nang took place over the South China. The color of the water changed from cobalt to sapphire and then azure blue. As a student, seeing Da Nang for the first time was an experience second to none.

Our arrival there took place during the first few days of the TET Offensive, which was a series of brutal attacks on many of the ground Army and Marine bases located throughout South Vietnam. Gunfire could be heard on the perimeter and way too close. Smoke was on the end of the runway. Numerous air-strikes were being run off of tower frequency. As such, planes were continuously taking off from all runways. F-4 Phantoms. A-4 Skyhawks. OS-10 weather planes. It was frenetic and just crazy.

There was a continual line of planes waiting to take-off toward the north from the seaward runway and to the south from the landward runway. Planes at Da Nang took off twenty-four hours a day. Those bound for North Vietnam for MiG cap always took off to the north, regardless of which direction everybody else was departing.

There were all kinds of planes in the pattern, accelerating up and zipping by you in one direction and while you were coming in from the other. As an arriving craft, there was simply no way to make a radio call. On our first pass, we just flew over the field to scope things out.

"This is Sierra Delta zero two requesting clearance. Over."

No answer from tower.

"Again, this is Sierra Delta zero two. Requesting clearance for our ferry of A-4s. Thanks. Over."

No answer.

Then, "Damn, just loop around again. Find a spot and just go in."

"Shit."

Had we not entered the flight pattern and landed without clearance from the tower, we might have been circling with waning fuel for hours. And that was our first experience into Vietnam.

I was relieved. I had survived my first overseas, re-fuel, prolonged excursion into a war zone. That should count for something right? Wrong.

We had gotten there. But getting home would require a whole different ball game. With only Class 4 orders, we came just ahead of stowaways.

"You guys did a great job getting over here. The bad news is, you gotta find your own way back home."

Hearing Captain Wilson, one of my flight instructors way back in Meridian share this insight was stunning. We were in a war zone.

"Just catch a hop on whatever ride you can," he remarked.

What the hell? Right.

Not wanting to wait around in a war zone, especially during the TET Offensive, I went into action. Forty minutes later we hitched a ride on a C-130 to Cubi Point. Then, a couple of us caught a hop on a station plane from Cubi to Clark AFB. Next we hitched on a private plane owned by a railroad back to San Francisco. Finally, we managed a hop from San Fran to San Diego and then to Travis on Bonanza Airlines. But only after being checked by security to see if we were allowed to fly with the pistols and explosive ordnance we used for emergency conditions if lost over the ocean. It was wartime people.

A bus took us back to Yuma. Relieved to finally be 'home' again in Arizona, upon reporting for duty, I arrived back at the squadron and had the final copies of my new orders. My ferry service back and forth to Vietnam would go on for several months.

"Lt. Lathrop, here's your new duty station," the Lt. Commander thrust the set of papers in my direction. "Good work out there. Your experience in Da Nang will come in handy."

"Oh?" was all I could manage.

"Yes siree. Well done. After a few more ferries, you're going to Vietnam."

As I looked down at the black and white telex ink, I could see these were not temporary orders. I had received a permanent change of station with orders to fly for thirteen months with the Fleet Marines of VMA-311 in WestPac. WestPac meaning Vietnam. What was I going to tell my wife?

Chapter 3

Being a Marine or Navy wife isn't easy. More than any other service, separations and deployments are long. At most winging ceremonies, the wives are given a special recognition by the Commanding Officer. The token is sometimes a certificate of appreciation or a pendant with Naval aviator's wings. Hearing the verbal recognition is honorable and appreciated, but it doesn't begin to address the anxiety, stress and loneliness felt by the spouse left behind.

But it was worse for the Marine wives. They were not allowed to stay on base as were the Navy wives. So there wasn't the support of the wives' clubs. The few Marine pilot wives that were there had to go home. Wherever home might be.

My wife, Janet, never seemed to get over the separations. From the minute I brought home news of my next deployment, she would go into a funk. Moody, irritable. Nothing I could say or do would pull her out of them. I knew today would be no different.

As I pulled my 1957 Ford pickup truck into the driveway of our apartments, I wished I had stopped at the Officer's club for a stiff Jack Daniels before coming home. I stayed out in the truck for several minutes. I knew what was coming. The crying. The cursing at the unfairness of the Navy. The screaming at President Johnson for not ending the war. It wasn't going to be a pleasant evening for sure.

When I married Janet two years prior, she knew what she was getting into. She was young, barely twenty. I had fallen in love with her perky personality and sweet smile. Having finished secretarial school, she was now working at the local bank as a teller.

No matter how many times you go over how hard and lonely deployments are going to be, some wives just don't understand it. I believe they're thrilled to be on the arm of a man in uniform. The whole pilot thing. But separation anxiety runs deep. At first, they get support from family and friends. But days run into weeks. Weeks into months. This time I had been gone for about six weeks. I wish she had been on base with the other wives. But Marines went over to 'Nam as individual replacements, the Navy went over as squadrons. As such, we had an apartment off-base. So she really didn't have the support that the Navy wives did who lived amidst other squadron wives on base. As a Marine wife, she felt she didn't fit in.

Opening the truck door, I took a deep breath. It was now or never.

"Hey, honey. I'm home." I called out.

"How's my handsome jet jockey?" she came over to hug me.

"Alright, I guess. Safely back on the ground."

"How was the trip? And the war? Was it scary?"

Scary was an understatement.

"It was pretty crazy. Especially Da Nang."

"Where's that? Vietnam, right?"

"Yep. One of the major air bases in South Vietnam."

Janet was scurrying around the kitchen. She loved to cook. She continued to chatter away as she pulled a casserole from the oven. Her soft, blond curls were hair-pinned up into a loose bun. Her light blue eye shadow matched her light blue short shorts. She had a white apron with small, little daisies on it tied around her waist.

"I made you your favorite. Lasagna."

"Smells delicious, honey."

"Nothing I wouldn't do for my man. Just so glad you're home. I hate it when you're away. I just don't know what to do with myself."

Just then, my son toddled over and grabbed onto the leg of my flight suit.

"Dadda. Dadda."

Picking him up, I was reminded of what life was really all about. I ran my fingers through his soft, sandy blond curls. Arty was named after my uncle, Arthur Lathrop. But Janet wanted my name in there too, so we added Gene to the middle. Arty had the "W" to a set of building blocks in his hands. He didn't so much build with them as shove them into his mouth. He was teething.

"Arty's been a terror with those teeth coming in. I've tried all the wives tales, but he wails up a storm."

"All part of growing up," I acknowledged. It dawned on me how much of our young son's life I had already missed being gone for training and missions. And now I would be gone for thirteen long months. "That sure smells good, honey."

"I wanted to make you something special. Because," she smiled and winked. "I've got some wonderful news."

"I've got some news, too." But it sure wasn't wonderful. Now I would spoil her happy outlook. It was only then that I noticed her face was glowing. I went over to her and wrapped my arms around her tiny waist. "Okay, out with it. You know I hate being taunted."

"I was going to wait until after dinner. But I just can't. Oh, Gene, it's wonderful news. We're expecting again."

"Really? Well, you must just be Fertile Myrtle."

"You're happy about it right?"

I gave her a big hug. "Of course."

"Maybe it'll be a girl this time. Oh, Gene. I hope. I hope. I've always wanted a little girl."

"As long as it's healthy honey. That's all that matters."

"Then, we'd be done. A little matched set of a boy and girl. Wouldn't that just be perfect?"

"How far along are you?" I asked trying to do the math in my head. Shit. Any way you figured it, I would be in Vietnam when the baby was born.

How long had it been since we'd had sex? It wasn't Janet's favorite thing to do. But as a dutiful wife, she acquiesced to my occasional needs. It wasn't bad sex, but I often wondered if she really enjoyed it. I was a simple man. A man who was loyal and loving and faithful. But a little excitement in the bedroom sure wouldn't have hurt.

"So, I've told you my news. What's yours?" she asked as she sat the lasagna down at the perfectly set table. I ran my finger around the lip of the orange matching plates. Janet put Arty in his high chair. How was I going to tell her?

"Let's enjoy this delicious meal, honey. I know you've worked hard. My news can wait."

"Now, Robert Gene Lathrop. I shared mine. I demand to know yours. Did you get a promotion?"

I turned the fork around, over and over on the orange and white placemat, thinking about a story that my grandfather had told me. 'Always keep your fork. For the best is yet to come,' he'd say.

"Come on now. Tell me. Tell me do."

I looked up at her happy face, knowing that what I was about to tell her would crush her. How do you tell your wife that not only would I be deployed to war, but miss the birth of our next baby?

"I saw the CO today. Seems my orders came in while I was ferrying the plane to 'Nam."

"Oh, where are we going? Out of this godforsaken desert, I hope. Back to the coast? East or West?" she excitedly asked.

All I could do was look at her, knowing my next words would be crippling. I swallowed hard and just told her.

"No, honey. I'm sorry. I am being deployed to Vietnam."

Her face became crestfallen. She slammed her fists down onto the table. "No, no, no!" she screamed. Getting up from the table, she ran to our bedroom and threw herself on the bed.

Following her inside, I sat down beside her, rubbing her back as she sobbed. There really wasn't anything I could say. I couldn't say it was going to be okay, because I knew it wasn't. I let her just cry while I continued to rub her back. Her face was buried in the pillow. I knew it was going to be a long night and an even longer period of lamentations until my actual departure date.

I got about twenty days leave before my tour. During that time, I had to move my pregnant wife home to Washington. The night before I left, I took my young son to the mountains with a friend of mine. I wanted to show him all of the places I had grown to love as a boy. After all, I might not make it back. My buddy and I stayed up all night and drank champagne and other beverages until about three AM. I slept for a couple of hours and then headed to the base.

It was pretty hard. I was already injured and my back still hurt. But I climbed on that plane and took one last look out at the mountains of Washington that I loved. Just as the plane took off, I shifted my focus. You just sort of have to shut off what's going on in your head. I think that's what most people going to Vietnam did. You couldn't live in two worlds at once. It just wouldn't work. I pulled down the shade and just blocked out everything.

Chapter 4

∞ March 20, 1968 Da Nang , Vietnam ∞

The Southern Airlines transport plane was in the first stages of the approach to Kadena, Okinawa. Myself and four other officers were seated in the front of the aircraft as requested by the flight attendant. We had been on the same draft since we left from Norton Air Force Base in Riverside, California five days prior to our arrival. I was surprised to find that I was the senior officer on the DC-8 that was taking 243 individual replacements to I Corps.

The I Corps Tactical Zone was a corps of the Army of the Republic of Vietnam (ARVN) that existed from 1955 to 1975. It was an area that stretched from the northernmost region of South Vietnam up to the border of North Vietnam beyond the demilitarized zone. It was one of four corps of the ARVN. This geographically marked the de-militarized zone or DMZ. The DMZ was a stretch of about a hundred miles. Only a couple of kilometers wide, it became important as the battleground of demarcation separating North Vietnamese territory from South Vietnamese territory.

As the officer in charge, I was given a manifest and the responsibility of getting them safely to Okinawa. On the trip over, thankfully, I had sealed the Honolulu Airport. I found that seven of the draft enlisted men had tried to buy tickets back to the U.S.

They were dropped off in Kadena, the big air base in Okinawa and locked up at Camp Hanson. The rest of us got all of our shots, which made most of us sick. We trained for immediate action, familiarizing ourselves with the M-16 rifle, having to be prepared for combat upon arrival at Da Nang.

We also got a briefing on Vietnamese culture and a history of the Buddhist religion. The instructors explained how Buddhists related to each other through self-enlightenment. That they considered their village to be another world. I thought it was strange how they described the Vietnamese as not sharing the same beliefs as Americans. There was no "do unto others." They explained that the Vietnamese would use their own people as shields against the enemy. We were also told about the frustrations of soldiers watching some villages with women and children being blown up, yet other villagers were allowed to peacefully work their rice paddies.

The Sergeant put in a reel to reel film of a Vietnamese woman from south of Chu Lai. The interviewer began asking her direct questions.

"Where have you been?"

"Everywhere," her tiny voice answered.

"You've been out of Vietnam, then?"

"No."

"Have you ever been to Saigon?" Saigon is about 300 miles south of Chu Lai.

"No."

"Well, have you been to Quang Ngai?" Quang is about five miles south of Chu Lai.

"No."

"Have you seen the ocean?" The South China Sea is just over the hill past Chu Lai.

"No."

"Have you been to another village?"

"No."

"Then where have you been?"

"Everywhere."

It took me a while to process. But what she meant was that she had been everywhere within herself. Where most GIs thought the Vietnamese to be uncaring, I realized it was just part of their basic religion and belief system. They didn't relate to another village. Their connections were blood relations and another village simply wasn't relevant. It didn't exist.

Vietnam wasn't a country, it was a series of hamlets held together by a border. The various villages were controlled by landlords owning the land. No wonder our GIs and our government leaders didn't understand them as a people. Their way of life was alien to most of them. My training as an intelligence officer helped me to understand.

During my flight training there were some South Vietnamese students. At the time, I found their interpersonal communication odd. But I learned about a concept called saving face. In essence, everything that the Vietnamese people did had to have honor in it. During training, I watched as orders were barked to them and they would just go blank, appearing not to be paying attention. It frustrated the hell out of officers who didn't understand. But other officers, with this awareness would keep them in a situation allowing them to save face. They knew that if the student lost it, you could scream at them until you were blue in the face, but get no response. I hoped that knowledge and appreciation would help me deal with the atrocities of war that I knew were coming.

The other four officers and most of the enlisted Marines were going to the Marine Air Wings. The two Captains were pilots and the Warrant Officer was a maintenance officer assigned to a helicopter squadron at Hue/Phu Bai, some twenty miles north of Da Nang.

As we made our final approach to Da Nang, which I had left less than eight weeks before, I watched the Phantoms and F-

106s taking off in rapid succession toward us on the north runway seaward. The other pilots marveled at the complete chaos of garbled radio chatter and continual jet wash.

Our jetliner rolled out and parked near the old French terminal on the north mat of the west runway, waiting for someone to tell us exactly where we were to go. All of us had orders, but the flight attendant relayed a message from the pilot of our aircraft that we were to remain on the plane until we were told what to do.

Thankfully, the air conditioning was left on for the five or ten minutes it took to bring a liaison officer aboard. It was a muggy eighty-five degrees outside, but with the sun radiating off the tarmac, it felt closer to a hundred. We had the option of looking at nothing but the inside of the airliner, or looking out at the craziness of Da Nang Air Station through the small round windows.

A C-123 was unloading casualties from a recent battle in the northern part of I Corps. There must have been fifty wounded soldiers, mostly covered in blood-tinged white bandages. Most, if not all, were ambulatory.

As I watched them, I thought of the casualties I had seen in the hospital at NAS Corpus Christi, as well as the ones I had seen up until 1947 in Walla Walla. I was surprised at the lack of emotion I felt while watching them. But even more so, at my fellow passengers' shell shock as they confronted the realities of war that they were now facing.

The enlisted Marines were separated from the enlisted personnel from the Army, Navy and Air Force. They were driven off in a minibus to be taken to the choppers that would carry them to their bases. The plane now near empty, the air conditioning had long been shut off.

The cabin area where we were sitting had become like a furnace before they finally let us off the plane. My armpits dripped with sweat under my dress uniform. The three other officers were met by a vehicle from Marine Air Group 36. I was left on my own to get to Chu Lai, some forty-three miles south.

Since I had just left Da Nang, I knew my way around enough to know how to get from one place to another. As the roads were far from secure, one had to travel from base to base by air. Each major base had an air freight facility that handled all of the cargo that was transferred from base to base. So, it was to Marine Air Freight on the west side of Da Nang for which I set out.

The heat on the mat in front of the old terminal was suffocating. I felt my shoes sticking to what must have been more than 120 degrees on the concrete mat. Picking up my B-4 bag and my flight gear, I started out for the nearest road.

Within five minutes, I was picked up by a six by six, five-ton Army truck and luckily was able to ride the rest of the way to the north side of the Da Nang Air Station, past graves and registration and over to the Marine Air Freight terminal near the hangar area for Marine Air Group (MAG) 11.

It was now nearly 1600 hours. There were no aircraft expected until the next afternoon headed south to Chu Lai. Not realizing that I could have stayed at Marine Air Group 11 transient officers barracks, I walked over to the transient quarters that were available to anyone near the Marine Air Freight building.

Why the higher-ups would have located the transient quarters where they did, I couldn't imagine. The Southeast Asia hut, with tin corrugated roof and screened sides, was located at the focal point of air activity on the Marine side of the base.

After depositing my possessions on one of the dozen bunks, which were without blankets, I noticed the effects of months of use under the filthy conditions that prevailed around the Da Nang area. Disgusting. I made my way to the nearest mess hall. It was a temporary one near the Marine flight line. Da Nang was nothing but red, dusty roads and storage areas. The odor of jet fuel permeated the air. As well as the pungent, smarmy smells emanating off bodies of who knows how many Marines, soldiers and sailors passing through from one field command to another.

The building was perhaps fifty yards from the main taxiway that all jet aircraft on the west side of the base used to taxi in and out of the MAG 11 line. Now late in the afternoon, the one hundred degree heat was augmented by the jet blast of Phantoms and A-6 Intruders taxiing in and out of the flight line. Blowing their exhaust through the screened sides of the hut added thirty or forty degrees to the stifling temperature, and deafening those staying within.

Since the aircraft operations continued around the clock, attempting to sleep was near impossible. I lay on the dirty mattress, trying to relax amidst the smell of the jet wash, combined with the roar of the Phantoms going into afterburner. Meshed in with all of that were the sounds of fellow transient occupants playing guitars and cleaning uniforms for R and R. Wide awake, I wondered what the flares overhead were for and where the distant machine gun and artillery fire was directed.

I got only about two hours of sleep tops, despite being up for more than thirty-six hours prior. Waking near midnight, the deafening sounds of the air war continued. During the ninety degree humid night, now all sweaty and grimy, I got up still clothed in my cotton utilities and went over to the Marine Corps hangar, some 100 yards to the north. It was lit up inside by large fluorescent lights so that the maintenance crews could work around the clock to prepare aircraft for flight. They also repaired gripes the pilots had written up or other maintenance crews had noted during pre-flights.

Walking over to the lighted area, I stood in the doorway. Two Marines, wearing dirty utilities and half covered with grease, were working to arm an A-6 Intruder. They sputtered and raged-on using their normal, far from professional terminology that I had heard used to obtain everything from another helping of food in the mess hall, to a complex electronic test device for radar.

"Hey, asshole, get that motherfucker over there, will you? I need that cocksucker to fasten this thing together."

"Fuck you, get it yourself. What do you think I am? Your cock sucking nigger? If you want the son of a bitch, get it yourself!"

It was good to be back with the harsh reality of the Marines. There was no use in wasting words that you couldn't understand when you didn't need to. Welcome back to Vietnam.

Chapter 5

∞ March 21, 1968 ∞

Still sleepless, but functioning, I had to wait at Marine Air Freight until 1400 before I could get my ride to Chu Lai. My attachment was to MAG 12, more specifically with VMA-311, nicknamed The Tomcats.

The terminal at Da Nang was a large, sheet metal building seventy-five by forty feet in width. The only furniture inside the building was a desk at the west side of the building. When you were waiting to fly out, you had the comfort of whatever you were carrying to use as a pillow and the concrete floor as a bed.

Most personnel travelling were exhausted Marines, soldiers and sailors, evenly spaced around the building. All were impassive while waiting to go somewhere that few of them desired to be - their duty station in I Corps. Interspersed among the active duty were Vietnamese men and women with their blackened teeth sitting with their arms around their knees with feet and buttocks on the ground. I could never understand how they could sit like that for long periods of time.

When a plane or helicopter arrived, the air freight duty NCO would take a manifest from the counter and call off the names of the next group of persons to be airlifted to the air station or the aircraft they were going to. Five or six planes, C-130s, C-

123s and a CH-46 helo took loads of waiting troops from the terminal.

"Johnson, E. Frankel. Gonzalez. Woodcock. Stockton. Davis, J. Halliburton. Schwartz." he rattled off. As he finished calling out about forty names bound for Hue/Phu Bai, Dong Ha and Khe Sanh, a low moan passed over the group still waiting. Not their turn. But I was thankful not to be going with that group, as the area was still heavily under siege.

I missed the first flight to Chu Lai, but at around 1400, a Marine C-117, which was a converted C-47 with longer wings, bigger engines and a stretched fuselage, arrived. Finally, I was given a seat. We took off with five passengers bound for Chu Lai.

We flew just off the yellow sands of the coast, southward forty-three miles to the Marine Air Station located on the large Army base of Chu Lai. As we flew, I had a good view of the coastal plain and the first five miles inland. The ground was torn up from various combat actions. Craters and smoldering piles of rubble were scattered everywhere. It was possible to see both jet aircraft and helicopters flying to and from targets, or operating tactically, attacking them. We were only flying at 1500 feet and one could see details of the villages, roads and the small Vietnamese fishing boats along the shore.

I could see the outline of Chu Lai long before I could see any detail. It stood out from the surrounding green mountains and fields by its color. It wasn't green, but looked more like a big sand box from ten miles away. As we approached, I could visualize the tin roofed, brown buildings scattered in clusters along the main concrete runway that ran 160 degrees, parallel to the coast. A metal matting crosswind runway ran perpendicular to the concrete runway. A second matting strip was parallel to the first, but only a few hundred yards from the water. There was black smoke from the burning shitters billowing up from the ground.

Chu Lai was first established as a Marine post in 1965. The 9th Marine Expeditionary Brigade landed at Chu Lai to protect the airfield from possible communist attack. At first, the SeaBees installed only a short airfield for tactical support (SATS). This particular SATS consisted of a 1,200 meter runway with an aluminum surface of interlocking lightweight metal alloy planking, a catapult and a carrier deck-type arresting gear. It also included a tactical airfield fuel dispensing system. Later they built the longer, concrete strip.

As we rolled out on the tarmac, I looked out across the brown Southeast Asia huts and hangars noticing the revetments for the Phantoms and A-4 E Skyhawks. Along the strip were also the remains of several Phantoms which had flown their last flights. They had been cannibalized for parts and sat on the ground near midfield. One was burned. They had built-up dunes of sand and dust resting against their fuselages.

All the rest of the planes, except for those fueling, were in concrete and metal revetments with metal roofs to protect them from incoming mortar, rocket and artillery fire. What a sight. There were hundreds of aircraft.

We taxied to air freight, a small twelve by fourteen building on the taxiway on the north end of the field. As I got off, I looked around for someone with whom to catch a ride. I didn't know my way around Chu Lai. Not seeing a soul, I called the duty NCO to come pick up me, my flight gear and my personal baggage.

While I was standing at the air freight building, I was able to watch flight operations in progress. It seemed like there was a plane taking off or landing every ten to fifteen seconds. Damn it was busy.

Some didn't even stop after taxiing, but taxied into the take-off position at full speed, running up their engines and departing, all totally loaded with ordnance of different types. Interspersed in the pattern were CIA aircraft, C-46s, and one short take-off plane that I couldn't identify, that needed less than 100 feet to roll and take-off.

I had no idea how the tower could handle or control all of the aircraft I saw on this one small runway. But somehow, they managed. I must say that I was awed by the frenetic nature of the flight operations at Chu Lai. I thought it was crazy.

The most bizarre part were the landings. Navy pilots trap on a ship, catching the wire with their tailhook. Because of the short runway at Chu Lai and the powerful attack and fighter planes flown in and out, pilots were required to trap on the ground. Insane. Coming in for a landing like on a carrier and then catching the ground wires and arresting gear. As each plane landed, there would be sparks that shot up as metal hit metal. No wonder our planes got so beat up. The fact that those sparks were so close to jet fuel made the hair stand up on my neck.

Chief Warrant Officer, Gunner Weatherford, who was the maintenance chief of Attack Squadron 311 picked me up. As I canvassed the flight line, I took a big breath. Now I knew where I was going to be flying for the next six months or more.

Weatherford was driving with another Marine by the last name of Lathrop. Meeting another person with the same last name as I had was a surprise, but it had already happened before when two of us Lathrops were in flight training at the same time and at the same level. At least this Lathrop was enlisted and wasn't going to show up on the flight schedule and cause the same confusion that had occurred previously.

"It's a bit toasty sir," Gunner apologized. "But it's like this all the time here. Welcome to Chu Lai." He put his foot down on the gas of the jeep and we were off. We drove down the taxiway in the 100 degree plus heat to the MAG 12 flight line.

I met two of the pilots I would be flying with, plus the duty officer, and had a chance to look around the squadron area.

"It's not much, sir," CWO Weatherford pointed out.

"Looks like you've taken some hits."

"Yep. Here and there. We sure have, sir. Keep your head about ya."

Several hangars were in shambles. One was half gone, with the roof hanging down in the back. They gave little protection to the aircraft located within. Chu Lai had been the victim of a bomb dump some two months prior.

"It happened during the first few hours of TET. That was some bad-ass shit, sir. Be glad you missed it."

"Yes. I've heard." I looked at the ripped up metal. The attack happened around the time I was still ferrying aircraft from the states to Da Nang. So this was war.

We drove up to the squadron area and I turned in my orders. Gunner was giving me a rundown on every aspect of the base.

"That over there's the officers' mess. Then past that is the officers' barracks. Down near the beach is the USO club. Nice place, they just got a new manager. She's one hot chick from New Orleans and damn can she sing."

"You don't say," I mumbled.

"But it's mostly Americal that hang out there, sir."

Little of what he rattled off was registering. Exhausted, I was overwhelmed by the last twenty-four hours and my mind had absorbed all it could for a while.

I wasn't given an assignment to quarters the first day. Arriving in late afternoon, I was again relegated to the transient barracks, which consisted of one bed in the middle of a small Quonset hut. I slept for about two hours before being summoned to meet the Operations Officer and Commanding Officer, Lt. Col McCrary. I wondered what the day had in store.

In another hut, open at the sides, screened-in and with screened windows and a metal roof, I found the duty clerk who directed me to a small office with four desks. One of which belonged to the CO. I saluted.

"Good afternoon, Lieutenant Lathrop. Hope your trip wasn't too miserable."

"No, sir. Reporting for duty, sir."

"Welcome to VMA-311. Have a seat. I've had a look-see over your flight log book. Flight ops feels that you don't have enough flight time or experience to be a combat pilot."

The expression on my face must have given away what I was thinking. This CO was incredibly blunt.

"No need to worry. We've come up with a plan. Don't get too comfortable, you'll be shipping out for TDY at Iwakuni, Japan."

"Japan. But why can't I just train here, sir?" I thought of the grueling trip and thousands of miles and now I was going back?

"No time to train here. In Japan you'll get more flight time and be able to familiarize yourself with the A-4. With zero hours of combat in the seat, you're no good to me here. You'll be back when you've logged some more hours."

He was right, I had less than 110 hours in the A-4 and thirty of those hours had been over the ocean, flying in formation. I was less than eight months out of a Naval hospital and I had zero hours in the single seat A-4. I went to bed thinking about Japan and what it would be like to be stationed there instead of Vietnam.

I had no illusions about the glamour of flying in combat. In a way, I was elated to be going anywhere but where I now was. Thirteen months was thirteen months. All the time counted. I now knew what to expect here and therefore figured that going to Japan would be better.

Too tired to go to the Officers' club that had been built as the officers' mess to use when we were not flying, I retreated to my barracks. It was suffocatingly hot. My body was being devoured by mosquitoes. Soaking with sweat, I was already covered in red dirt from the roads of the base. Hmph. So much for Chu Lai. I fell asleep to the sound of afterburners yet again.

Chapter 6

∞ March 22, 1968 ∞

Bright rays of sunshine were peeking through the Quonset hut. Listening, I couldn't tell any difference in the flight operations from the night before. They simply never stopped.

I took a shower, which was one of the amenities of being in the air wing and not the infantry. We had one. After shaving, I put on some clean utilities and went to the officers' mess to eat.

The officers had built a grass-roofed, tile floored mess and club that looked like a large hut from *Gilligan's Island*. The Vietnamese used huts like this for gatherings like what would be a public meeting hall in the states. It was less than one hundred yards from the South China Sea and had an uncovered veranda where you could sit during the evening and look out over the sparkling azure blue water and endless stretches of sandy beach. The MAG 12 engineers who built it had taken the advice of the Vietnamese and constructed a thatched roof, without underlay. As such, it kept out the rain. MAG 13 hadn't trusted the native Vietnamese experience and had underlaid their roof with black plastic sheeting. Their roof had rotted almost immediately.

I ate with several of the other pilots with whom I attended flight training. There were only about eighty or ninety A-4 pilots at Chu Lai. Most had been stationed together before. As such, if you didn't come across someone you knew personally, you'd meet up with someone that they knew. Suter. Wilson. Sandlin. There were all there.

To anyone else, they club might have freaked people out. Just about everyone in there was armed.

"Crazy amount of ammo in here, huh Lathrop? Ron Suter remarked.

"Yeah. I came with mine too," referring to my .45.

"Wanna have a brewski with us?" he beckoned.

"Nah. Gonna go talk a walk."

Alcohol and firearms. What a mix. After chow, lots of them went next door to the O club to drink. Although I joined them on some occasions, mostly I sorta kept to myself.

After a quick bite, I walked over to Operations. I wasn't sure when I was leaving Chu Lai, but the way things had gone so far, I expected to be in Iwakuni by the following sunset. I was ready to leave at any time. The constant sound of artillery and the flares around the base at night were none too comforting. If I could avoid them for any period of time, I was happy to oblige.

Change is the unknown motto of the military. As I entered the hut, change is what greeted me as I saluted McCrary, the CO.

"There's been a change of plans Lieutenant. Japan's out."

"Oh, how is that, sir?"

"We've lost an A-4 pilot. Missed the damned arresting gear. All of them. So, you'll be taking his place."

"I see, sir. No problem."

From what I heard through the grapevine, two or three days before, a squadron pilot in a fully loaded A4-E had not reached airspeed at midfield and aborted. Not able to slow the plane enough with the brakes and missing the arresting gear, he ejected as the plane left the overrun. He died in the explosion that followed.

The squadron never had more than seventeen pilots to fly the twenty planes CWO Weatherford usually had available. The loss of one suddenly made me fully qualified to fill the cockpit he had left vacant. My new orders were stamped and I was given the written tests for the A4-E.

Previously, it had taken me a week or more to scope and learn the aircraft. I did it with the A4-E in one afternoon. Going through the tests, I found the model I had previously flown. It was different in some ways, but not in too many that would make flying the newer version difficult. An hour after taking the tests, I went out to the flight line and started up the aircraft. Noting the basic differences, I was deemed ready for flight as a wingman.

All pilots were given three familiarization flights in the TA-4F so that they could see the ground they would be flying over, learn the radio calls and learn the basics of flying in I Corps. My three flights were all at dusk or after dark.

I saw Da Nang off the port wing and Da Nang off the starboard wing. Stars above. Stars below. I heard all manner of radio calls. Some to us, some on guard and some to others. It was so confusing, I knew no more after three missions than I had known before flying them.

When I returned at midnight after the third flight, I saw my name on the flight schedule for two missions the following day. Again, welcome to Vietnam.

My first mission would be to the Khe Sanh, with a Captain Trumpfheller. I wondered if he was the same Trumpfheller I had known during my pilot training at Kingsville.

I knew Khe Sanh was under siege and had heard about the dangers of flying there. Dodging ground fire and surface to air missiles or SAMS. My first mission was to drop napalm and 500 pound retarded bombs. Primarily, I was flying as an advanced student, with zero hours in the A4-E. However, I was eerily confident. Probably more so than I should have been.

I was assigned my living quarters, which consisted of a hut next to the road near a Caterpillar generator. There were six officers in each hut and twelve enlisted Marines in a hut near the area where we slept. We were given sheets and a blanket, more to fend off the rats, bugs and mosquitoes than for warmth, which was definitely not a need.

Making up my bed and ready for a sleep, I put my pillow over my head to keep the mozzies at bay. Attempting to sleep, I tried hard not to think about anything except getting some rest. The incessant heat and constant noise were fatiguing in themselves. Even though you could barely shout above the generator, it wasn't as bad as trying to sleep through the sounds of the Phantoms I had heard taking off and landing at Da Nang.

As I drifted off to sleep, I wondered if I was in the bed vacated by the pilot who had been killed. When a pilot lost his life, it was as though they ceased to exist. None of the other pilots ever discussed it. The unspoken code of silence prevailed. I knew nothing about him, except how he had died. But I knew one thing for sure, that mistake would not be made by me.

A pilot should fly focused on every detail, plan to catch any problem before it happened and take appropriate counteraction. The problem with doing so was that you could lose your sensory awareness of the overall situation by continually focusing on minutiae. I vowed never to die doing what he did.

It was a simple plan. When I pushed the throttle forward and nothing adverse happened when I did so, I would be at the end of the runway. Then, I would make a decision of what to do with the plane at its maximum speed, regardless of any problems. If airborne, I would be turning over the land toward the South China Sea. If not, my wingman would have to avoid me, the seat and the explosion. I was not ever going to pull the power back and go off the runway at any speed but the maximum I could obtain. That was for sure. I had already seen several people killed analyzing what was going to kill them, instead of surveying the ground from their parachute and trying to avoid the cactus where they were going to land.

Somehow, I got through the first night. I was awakened at daybreak by the duty truck driver, Frenchy.

"Sir," he said gently shaking me. "Sir, it's time to get up."

"Right," I mumbled rolling out of bed. Time for my first combat flight in Vietnam.

Chapter 7

∞ March 23, 1968 Khe Sanh ∞

I met Captain Trumpfheller, a career Marine in the wee hours of dawn. As it turned out, he was indeed one of my former flight instructors from Kingsville. We greeted each other in the briefing room, which housed the air intelligence section.

"Gene. Great to see you again!" he reached out to shake my hand. "Let's get through this one with no ejections, okay?" he smiled with a wide grin. It felt good to see a familiar face. I felt comfortable with him.

Together, we got our target briefing from the Air Intelligence Officer. Next, our squadron six by six picked us up and we rode the two miles to the squadron area. The field near the briefing shack, where the Marines were once stationed had been taken over by the US Army and was now used by the 14th Aviation Battalion.

We bounced along and drove down to the eight by forty foot trailer sitting in front of the half-destroyed hangar. The Air Intelligence Officer (AIO) gave me a long brief, leaving out nothing. It took forty-five minutes.

I checked out an aircraft and pre-flighted it, checking the fuses on the 500 pound bombs and the napalm canisters. The plane captain helped me strap in the tiny cockpit. I checked over the switches, gave the signal for power and lit off the jet. This A-4 was a Navy plane that had been sent to the Marines as a replacement aircraft when the ship it was on deployed back to the United States from Yankee Station. Yankee Station was a geographic point in the Gulf of Tonkin off the coast of Vietnam used by the U.S. Navy aircraft carriers during WestPac cruises to launch strikes in the Vietnam War. The tail had been repainted with Marine call numbers and the VMA-311 tomcat logo.

The Marine ground crew looked exhausted. They wore tattered utilities which were covered with grease and dirt from working around the leaking hydraulic fluid, fuel and water from various tanks scattered around the periphery of the dusty flight line.

I received a call on Channel 1, the base ground frequency and taxied out following the lead.

"All systems go. Ready for take-off." The lead gave the thumbs-up.

I pulled up into position just aft of him, upwind of his jet wash. It must have been 150 degrees in the cockpit, since the air conditioner didn't cool the cockpit until the engine power was at eighty percent or above.

A-4 tail number Whiskey Lima 224-1, the lead plane for our mission number, dropped his hand, signaling that he was releasing his brakes and started rolling. I gave him thirty seconds and released my brakes. I rolled until I had 150 knots on my airspeed indicator and turned at less than 100 feet after I left the runway behind.

Turning inside toward the lead, who was turning wings level, I joined less than a mile from the take-off and the runway. Immediately, I got a signal to move out into cruise formation, a position where I could follow maneuvers without being previously signaled that they were going to happen.

As I settled into cruise formation, some fifty feet from the lead and well aft, there was a call from lead on the radio.

"Vice Squad. Vice Squad. This is Hellborne two two four lifting off Chu Lai. Request inflight following."

"Roger. Hellborne two two four, squawk emergency indent."

There was a pause as the lead hit the IFF button.

"I have your radar contact two two four. We have several planes at the 180 to the 200 radial of Da Nang TACAN from ground level to 5,000 feet."

"Roger," replied Dash 1, which was short for 224-1. We continued to fly up the coast to our point of landfall.

My plane was icing up inside the cockpit and I could not find the cabin pressurization switch. When I finally did, I almost blew out my eardrums when the cabin pressurized. The steam and ice disappeared and I could see out normally again.

I could see the coastal plain by looking past the lead aircraft. It was clear enough in the spring haze to see almost to the mountains. From 10,000 feet it was possible to see the land as well. It was so torn up. From the coast inland. There were scattered bomb craters, places where there was smoke from fires or artillery and shattered villages visible near the coast. There was constant chatter on the radio, both on Vice Squad and the guard frequency, supposedly used for emergency broadcasts and monitored by all aircraft.

As we approached Da Nang, I could see the constant flow of aircraft on the runway and in the air around the large air station. I now had a good idea how it lay in relationship to Chu Lai, as well as points north to North Vietnam. We flew for nearly half an hour, then turned inland just south of the DMZ. As we flew inland, I could keep the lead in sight and still look at what was below.

The ground was battered beyond belief. There were overlapping bomb craters from the coast inland. There was almost nothing that had not been bombed. I couldn't believe that so many bombs could have been dropped anywhere.

My sightseeing was over. There was all this radio traffic. People calling in artillery. I could hear naval gunfire and airstrikes from other planes over the radio. I could see those strikes going into Khe Sanh. Then I heard Dash 1 over the radio telling me to switch to a pre-coded frequency.

"Dash two up," I confirmed.

"Fingerprint one two, this is Hellborne two two four inbound with delta two and delta nines for your control."

This was the code for our 500 pound retarded bombs and napalm. Immediately, there was a reply from the small single engine O-1, an aircraft smaller than a Cessna 150 that was used as a target spotting aircraft by the Marines.

"Proceed inbound to the zero nine zero radial of Channel one zero nine, Hellborne. And hold," the pilot directed.

Dash 1 moved me into trail and I set all my armament switches that I could while moving back. I now was in a position to look at Khe Sanh, then surrounded and under siege by more than 40,000 North Vietnamese Army (NVA) regular troops.

I dropped back and set my flaps at one quarter to give myself a little more lift and surveyed the scene laid out below. The first thing that caught my eye was the small size of the Khe Sanh base. It looked like a piece of tape, red and torn, straddled across a small ridge surrounded by taller mountains. There were wrecked aircraft on the mat and I could see rounds impacting the ground inside the perimeter.

From the perimeter outward, there were concentric rings of trenches, blown apart and separated from each other by almost interlocking bomb craters. The hills surrounding the base to the north, Hills 881 north and 881 south, appeared to be in our possession. As did Hill 861, which I was shown in the briefing. The mountain of Coroc in Laos, overlooked the base from four or five miles and appeared to have caves in which artillery pieces could be located. There were air strikes being conducted by more than one air controller. The impact of bombs could be seen west toward Laos from where I was orbiting.

Flames from the shitters were burning. The mottled layout of the base was covered with bunkers waylaid with debris types I couldn't recognize from my altitude. Mounds of military material were stacked here and there.

The trenches stretched as far as I could see to the north and west. A bombed out road ran past Khe Sanh to the west. Alongside the road, just past the base on the way to the Laotian border, was a bombed out French-style building. Khe Sanh seemed like a benign name for the horror that I saw below.

Observation time was over as I heard the controller giving us our mission.

"Hellborne two two four, I have your mission. You ready to copy?" the self-assured and commanding voice queried.

"Roger," replied Dash 1.

"Run in heading will be zero six zero, left hand pull. Friendly forces will be at your eleven o'clock at 500 hundred meters at Khe Sanh. Ground fire is expected to be heavy."

"Roger that," Captain Trumpfheller answered. As Dash 1, he then read back the brief as it had been given. He was descending and maneuvering to a position so that he would be at the correct point when permission was given to roll in.

"Do you see my mark, two two four?"

Fingerprint had shot a smoke marker between the base of one of the mountains and Khe Sanh. I saw Dash 1 turn toward the smoke.

"Roger. Dash one in hot."

He started down the chute and toward the target with all switches armed. We were going to drop all our bombs and napalm on a single run. I was too far behind to roll in on the target as he called off. I watched as he rolled inverted, did a double half roll entry, leveled out and released over the target. Orange ground fire winked from his nine o'clock position abeam the target.

I pulled up on the run in line, watching the napalm from the previous air strike run behind the lead aircraft, but behind him and beneath him. Although I had been nervous going up, as soon as I came up to roll in, everything inside my cockpit turned dead calm. I turned on the run in line and rolled inverted, holding the gunsight rings above the smoke and moving 100 meters to the right as the controller had indicated.

Turning on my master armament switch, I pulled up on the run in line. As I started the run down to the target, suddenly time slowed to a crawl. Dash 1 was turning back to the left, the smoke and fire of his ordnance drop was gently drifting toward Khe Sanh. The target seemed too big to miss as I pulled the gunsight ring down below it and started rolling back into a wings level upright position.

Seconds elongated into slow motion. The area of smoke was so large, I couldn't miss it. I saw it get bigger and bigger in the gunsight picture. I saw no ground fire and never did when on a bombing run. I think I was too intensely focused on the target and hitting it.

I pressed the target until it looked like it was going to impact with the aircraft. Hitting the button on top of the stick, I pulled up and to the left, Khe Sanh above me a hundred feet or more.

Kicking my rudder hard left to see what was happening behind me, I could just catch the napalm and flame in the mirror on the right side of my canopy. The air controller, Fingerprint 12, was reading the bomb damage assessment (BDA) to Dash 1 before I even had time to get my armament switches off. I tried to find Dash 1 in the haze toward the coast near Dong Ha, which was the last place I saw him.

I was frustrated as hell. How could I write the BDA, fly the plane, look for my lead and get my cockpit in order all at the same time? When he had the BDA written down, he radioed.

"This is Hellborne two two four. Got me in sight Dash 2?"

Just as he did so, I caught sight of him at my one o'clock, just a little above me.

"Tallyho," I answered and joined in on a big black F-100 flying in the same approximate direction I wanted to go. I flew with him for a minute or two, then saw a single A-4 flying down the coast. Realizing I was following the wrong plane, I moved away from the Air Force F-100, I joined my lead.

As we flew back on Vice Squad frequency, I was more aware of what was around us than when we came up the coast the first time. I saw other aircraft using the same airway to and from the DMZ. I also got a better look at the location of the bases from the DMZ south to Chu Lai and a more comprehensive view of I Corps as a whole.

While still flying along the coast, we checked each other out visually for battle damage or hung ordnance. At ten miles, we descended from 8,000 feet. I was given the signal to drop back and I followed the lead onto the runway and to the flight line.

One mission and I felt totally drained. The insufferable heat taxiing, the stress of trying to meet the demands for the first time, and the buildup of fatigue in just getting to Vietnam left me almost totally exhausted.

There wasn't much of a debrief. There wasn't enough time. Before I had a chance to get out of my torso harness and G-suit, a Major who I did not know from the group headquarters came over.

"Are you ready to brief Captain Weatherford?"

I must have given him a quizzical look. He looked at me like I had been there forever.

"We're, as in you and me, are going back to the same place you've just come from."

I couldn't believe it but we did. It was a lot easier the second time, than the first.

After debriefing from my second mission to the Khe Sanh and DMZ areas, I took off my flight gear, went into the ready room and got a beer. Walking around to the office of the Intelligence Clerk, I met my assistant.

"Corporal Crowley. Nice to meet ya. I'm your new Intelligence Officer. I thought you might show me around and give me the scoop on what's expected in the job."

"Yes, sir. Be glad to, sir."

Being assigned as the Intelligence Officer of a squadron was no present. No one cared what you did until you lost a classified document.

"It's not bad, sir. But lose a record? Then the full force wrath of the entire organization will rain down on ya. My advice?"

"Sure, Corporal. I'm sure you know."

"Best you can do, if you do everything right, is not to be noticed by no one."

"Got it."

Chapter 8

As a Marine pilot, the expectation was that you would have a second job. I requested this one. I had some Intel training and thought it would be way more interesting than working as an officer in Operations, Maintenance, or any of the other desk jobs in the squadron.

With the science background I had, finding unknowns from the study of facts was natural for me. That's all intelligence work involved. Fact finding. I liked doing the work and most of the pilots I knew avoided it like the plague.

"There's really just three parts of the job, sir. You keep track of the classified documents as they come in. Register them in the register, here. And dispose of them when they're no longer needed. That's the main part."

"I see. Sounds easy enough."

"It can get complicated, sir. But you'll find that out for yourself."

I knew the penalty for losing a classified document. It was a permanent black mark on one's record. Looking around the room at the stacks of paper, I could see it was going to take a lot of time to keep track of the documents we had.

"One more thing, sir."

I looked up from the papers I was thumbing through.

"Should the base get overrun. We gotta destroy all the documents PDQ."

"Got it."

Surveying the room, I knew the very first thing we were going to do was simplify the record keeping system. It was a total mess. There were documents that were out of date and not used which were generally taking up space.

"Crowley. Get some paper. We're gonna start a burn list."

"As in fire, sir?"

"Yep. We're gonna burn what we don't need and get this chaos cleaned up."

"Yes, sir. Burn baby burn," Crowley flashed a wide grin.

Several hours of culling and burning took care of the massive overload of record keeping. Now I could spend what time I had on intelligence reading of the new reports that came in and analyze them for the squadron.

The reports ran the gamut. Some were daily summaries of what happened on the base perimeter. Others analyzed various military actions occurring throughout the eastern hemisphere. I didn't get back to my hooch until nearly midnight after my first day of flying and had a brief at 0600 the next morning.

Once I started reading, I wasn't at all comfortable carrying knowledge I had over North Vietnam and Laos day after day and night after night. Flying over I Corps, seeing combat and talking to those engaged on the ground, I then would come back and read the reports given by the Third Marine Amphibious Force at Da Nang. This gave me a unique overview of what was actually happening that few people had. The rest of the pilots simply flew their missions. Reading the reports, I wondered if knowing the real story was a good idea or not.

Between flying, standing the duty, doing the intelligence work and taking care of the mundane jobs that always cropped up, there was little time left for sleep. I started doing the work in Intel when I was standing duty at night. At three in the morning, even when we were flying a night schedule, I could find time to work in the office.

The Commanding Officer wanted me to keep him informed of anything important via three daily reports. I also kept a map for the pilots of the latest known locations of all the small units around Chu Lai and the larger units all the way from Quang Ngai, fifteen miles to the south up to the DMZ.

As an added role, Colonel McCrary had me brief the enlisted marines on the way we flew, the equipment we needed and how we used it. I also told them about the locations of enemy units and what we saw when we flew against them. I was surprised at their response.

"Dang, man. I had no idea."

"You're shitting me."

"One helluva war, man," were some of the more select phrases. But they also expressed an appreciation for knowing more than what they saw on the flight lines. As ground crew they hadn't understood how the equipment they armed the pilots with was used over the targets. They were just doing their dirty jobs.

Once they understood how important each instrument, arming system and components of ordnance were to the success or failure of the missions we flew, they took an entirely different approach in attitude to what they did. At least in our squadron. Our aircraft crews of VMA-311 were simply the best. I trusted them with my life.

It was a shock to their system to know about the conditions just outside the perimeter. They simply had not been aware of how close the war actually was to the base. A couple of people had been captured by the Viet Cong less than a hundred meters from the wire.

Chapter 9

One of the spots at Chu Lai which was a welcome relief was the USO club. In early 1968, they were primarily managed by official female volunteers, most of whom were given a rank of GS10, or Captain. Most of the guys thought they were members who had stayed on in Vietnam, sometimes after tours with Bob Hope to help support the troops. In a rare instance that was the case.

Chu Lai's USO was a ramshackle hut of liquid relief. It was literally built on the beach butting up to the South China Sea. As such, it served as a surf club, bar and grill for when officers and enlisted sought relief from the company mess. Built up on stilts above the sand, you could sit out on the veranda and watch the sampans in the South China Sea. The beauty of the beach at Chu Lai was in such contrast to the bombed out devastation I had seen inland.

There was a tall water tower with the blue USO sign. The veranda was built up on stilts for when the surf came in. Sometimes acts would perform outside. They were mostly local Vietnamese bands. Every once in a while, some USO showgirls in scantily clad, spangly outfits and knee high white boots would perform. The club, like the O'club reminded me of something you'd see in Hawaii. As far as USO clubs went, it was very nice.

Inside were ping pong tables, orange and other colored plastic sixties style chairs. I remember a full length poster of

Betty Boop tacked to the wall. What I liked most were the mini-skirts that the USO volunteers wore routinely. It was nice to see some legs.

As the war escalated, so did the need for USO Clubs. They were staffed with educated young women, many with degrees in theater, broadcasting or recreation. Knowing the risks, these young women signed up for the longest volunteer tours in Vietnam, eighteen months.

Although ranked, they were not required to wear a uniform. Civilian clothes only. Mostly the mini dress. No slacks were allowed. They were told upon arrival in Vietnam that no matter what they saw, the men were never to see them cry. Their sole purpose? According to their executive director was to be happy. Maybe that's why staffers at USO clubs got R and R every three months. The stress would do one in otherwise.

When I first got to Chu Lai, there wasn't really a place to wash up. So after hours and hours of flying, smelling so bad, I would get out of my plane, grab a bar of soap, soap up and go out to the ocean for a swim in my flight suit and underwear and everything. After awhile my flight suits became all stiff and everything. The bigger USO clubs had showers, but not at Chu Lai.

The current manager was a stunning woman. She stood about five foot eight. Of slender build, with a flawless olive complexion and a significant rack, she was welcome eye candy and relief to the atrocities of war.

"Hey there Marine. Are you lost?" she referred to the fact that I was one of only a handful that weren't Army inside the club. "You know I can get some local gals to do your laundry."

"Nah. I'm doing just fine."

"Guess it depends on who's making that judgement call," she said in her sultry voice, taking a look at my salt water drenched flight suit. "So much for a man in uniform," she smirked.

I found her to be enchanting. Over time we became friends and confidants. Like many bartenders, she was one of the few people in Nam that I felt I could truly talk to. No judgment, just honest relating of things that just made your stomach churn.

In other circumstances, had I not been married, I would have jumped her bones. But she wore her heart on her sleeve for an A-4 Navy pilot who had recently been relo'd to the USS Bon Homme Richard, affectionately known as the Bonnie Dick. As such, I kept my respectful distance. On deployment, I was one of the few who did.

"How's your stick time on the A-4 been?"

"Good. Just flying samo, samo. And how's your club time?"

"Good. Bad. You name it, I've heard it all this week."

"Guess you hear all kinds of stories."

She gave me a knowing look. "You could say that."

Coming from around the table behind me, she supplied me with a much needed platonic shoulder massage. How did the USO have such a knack for selecting and recruiting these wonderful women who knew just how to care for the guys on their base?

"She's a real looker isn't she?" another pilot took a seat next to me at the table. The patch on his flight suit read VA-212. Navy.

I wasn't really looking for company, but decided to be friendly. "Yeah. But I'm married."

"Me too, but it never hurts to look," he chuckled taking a chew on his cigar. "Never."

"You on TDY?"

"Yeah. Just dropped off what's left of an A-4 to MAG 12."

"Oh, yeah? I'm flying with the Tomcats."

"She's gonna take some re-working. We beat her up pretty bad. Wing flap got hit over I Corps." He was looking over at all the pinball machines. And the USO gals. "Nice club."

"Yeah, but I feel like a minority," I answered looking around at all of the Americal guys. The Navy pilot finished up his drink and moved to the other side of the room. There was an avionics tech sipping on a beer. At least he wasn't Army.

"You're with VMA-311?" I said looking at his patch.

"Yessir."

"You all do a darned good job keeping our birds up and going."

"Yep. It ain't easy. – 'specially when those Navy jockeys rip 'em up." He glanced over at the Navy pilot now flirting with one of the USO gals.

"Buy you another beer?"

"Thanks, sir. You're alright for an officer."

"No. Thank you. I know you guys take good care of us."

"Mostly the planes, sir. Just doin' the job."

Boy was I ever thankful for that. I had a family to go home to. It was going to be a long thirteen months.

"Thanks for the beer, sir. I know you're not supposed to really hang with us enlisted."

"We're all one team, Marine."

"Damned straight, sir. Damned straight."

Chapter 10

∞ April 9, 1968 Japan ∞

At 0700, I flew as a wingman to the Da Nang area. The pre-flight briefing in the squadron area before flying was normally given by the flight leader. But today it had been shortened to the radio frequencies and pointing to the door.

It was tiring to fly continually the way we did. Flying two missions a day, working on other things and standing duty at night caused little things to be overlooked and never completed. Sometimes I didn't know the pilot with whom I was flying. We were so busy that pilots from other units joined us, just to get in their flight time. Attached to units other than Chu Lai, they flew with us a few days, logged their time and then returned to their squadrons.

About the only thing that changed from mission to mission was the ordnance load and location. The procedures getting to and from the target were always the same.

After my second mission of the day, up near the Hue/Phu Bai Marine Base, I landed and was met by a Major Durham and another Major. I saluted.

"Lieutenant Lathrop. You've been chosen for some TDY."

"Pack your bags, because we'll be leaving in less than an hour for Japan," the other Major stated.

"Japan, sir?" I questioned. Not again.

"Yes, Lieutenant. You're being sent to sea survival school with the 5th Air Force. Just south of Tokyo at Numazu."

"I see. I'll be ready, sir."

"Righto, Lieutenant."

I barely had time to get out of my flight gear, get my B-4 bag packed and get into some utilities. I couldn't get rid of my pistol, so I just put it on.

Seven hours after boarding an aircraft at Chu Lai Air Freight, I found myself standing in Tokyo International Airport. I was a sight in red dusty Marine utilities, carrying a red dusty B-4 bag, wearing a .38 pistol. I was only separated by two or three yards from everyone else in the busy terminal. I stayed with the two Majors whom I had accompanied because they knew their way around.

We boarded an Air Force bus that went from the air terminal to the base at Tachikawa where we each got a room in the transient BOQ. I plopped down on the bed. It was nearly midnight. Another crazy day. I started the day by briefing for a mission eighteen hours before. Now I had flown two missions, been on three different transport aircraft and now was 2,500 miles away from where I started.

Two days later, I was alone when I began the journey to Numazu. It was a good thing Major Durham had shown me the general direction of the train station the day before. They had both overslept from a night out with local girls. I had no idea where they were. I somehow had to navigate my way through Tokyo without knowing a lick of Japanese. Standing at six feet, I towered over a sea of black heads. As I walked up to the ticket counter, I handed the clerk in a train company uniform a handful of bills.

"Numazu?"

He took an amazingly few number of bills from the stack, handed me a small ticket covered with Japanese symbols and turned the hand of a large clock next to the window to 7:32. Next he pointed to a numbered post.

After setting my watch to the station time, I walked over and stood on the platform. At 7:32, a train pulled into the station, the doors opened and a horde of children dressed in blue school uniforms flowed off the train. The train was still packed. I got on, grabbed a leather strap in my hand and stood in the aisle as the train left the station.

The train was jam packed with people, about half of which were more blue uniformed students. I could see that there was nowhere to move. I had no idea where we were going, or which stop at which to get off. I took a chance and showed my ticket to a small uniformed boy.

"Numazu?"

He smiled and seemed pleased that I spoke to him. He pointed to his small watch and gave me a time to disembark. Then, he wanted to practice his English.

"You soldier. United States."

"Yes." It wouldn't matter that I explained that I was actually a Marine.

"Yankee. On boat? On plane? Fly?"

"Yes," I made the motion of flying with my arms. His English was far better than my Japanese, but we had a ways to go before we were ever going to talk at any length.

My one word greeting, *konnichiwa* and question *Numazu?* got me through to a central train station in Tokyo, Shinjuku and another concrete train platform at dusk. I rode trains for twelve hours when I handed my ticket to a slight, older Japanese gentleman standing at the post where I had just left. He pointed to the ground and then looked directly at me.

"Numazu," he grunted and walked away.

I hailed a taxi and survived a hair-raising ride to the small Air Force training facility outside of town on a beach near a bay off the ocean. It was freezing cold, windy and no place to be swimming for another three months.

We spent three days in lectures and made one freezing jump into the water to learn how to use a sea survival suit. I doubted that I could get into the tight cockpit of the A-4 with one on. I certainly was not going to wear one when the seawater temperature in South Vietnam was eighty degrees. So, I took the attitude of taking the course as more of a vacation than learning something I already knew. I had completed sea survival school in Florida.

On the fourth day, we learned how to pack a seat pack used on an ejection seat. Each of us was recovering from a long night of drinking. The three officers in the course, two Marine Majors and myself, were always the first to complete each assignment and task.

We had parachute riggers to rig our chutes in the squadron. I would never dream of packing my own. Had I been required to do so, I would never have flown. The one time I needed one, during my bail out and crash, it didn't work right anyway.

One by one, I picked up each of the articles that went into the seat pack. I stomped down on the top and managed to get it closed. A raft was on top and the shark repellent, sea dye and other small necessities were underneath.

As I stood next to mine, waiting for it to be inspected, the unexpected occurred. I was told to pick it up and go down to the beach. There was an outboard powered up. It was an open speedboat with a reel coming out the back and a parachute hooked to the end of a rope which was attached to a release mechanism.

Before I could think of any way to get out of the situation, I was hooked into the parachute. The rest of the class was briefed on how to use it while I was there.

Before I had worked up the courage to go on, the speedboat took off out to sea. I was lifted up in the chute with my seat pan strapped on in a survival suit. The shore quickly disappeared behind me.

When we had gone three miles into the choppy bay, I saw the crewman in the aft part of the boat wave his hand in a sweeping motion. Suddenly, I was falling fast into the dark sea.

Reluctantly, I pulled the release handle on the seat pack and looked down expecting to see all the contents drop into the sea and leave me to die, alone, in Japan. All because of my own ineptitude in packing a raft and seat pack.

I was overjoyed to see the raft and contents hanging below me, but not for long. Because just as I was assured I was not going to drown at sea, I hit the water and found myself tangled in the parachute shrouds.

With a single sweep of my right arm, I had the raft under me and the parachute unhooked and floating away. The raft was just big enough for my body. The water temperature was forty-nine degrees, but the survival suit kept me warm. What bothered me was that with the waves the way they were, I couldn't see land or any of my other sea survival school unfortunates nearby.

Taking out the shark repellent, I deployed it and the green dye. The dye stayed around the raft and dyed it and me green. Riding on top of one of the waves, I saw the mountains of Japan for the first time. I started paddling towards them. Unknown to me, a current was carrying me toward shore. It was about thirty minutes before I saw the beach in the distance. I drifted toward it and saw that I was going to land in front of a school.

All of the children had been let out to watch the fools swim in the ocean in late winter. As I drew near, I looked toward the area I thought the other pilots and crewman would be in their rafts. I couldn't see the Air Force encampment. Although I didn't know it then, I had been the first one dropped and therefore the farthest from the camp.

I let the raft drift up on the beach and got out. I was so disoriented, I had no idea which way to go back to the camp. I was on a spit of land and could have gone either way.

Initially the school children were well behaved and looked on silently at the yellow-green stained man in the flight helmet carrying the seat pan without comment or sniggers. What a strange mess I must have looked. Walking down the beach, I came to an older man leaning next to a retaining wall that prevented the beach from eroding further. I intended to ask him which way to go.

Now the children were laughing and pointing. I wondered what had caused them to do so. But then I saw the man. He had his pants down and was masturbating while looking at me and smiling. I simply turned and continued to walk down the beach wondering what other weirdness the day had to offer.

Muttering to myself, I decided that was the last survival training I was going to attend. Four was enough. I was going to learn how to avoid such turmoil again. I would develop my own survival techniques long before attending other schools, because I would start the survival by never having to go there.

I was never more miserable than when starving, freezing, cold and wet or being eaten in the jungle by everything in it which bit, stung, slimed, or threw things at you. I realized today had been just as miserable as the first survival school. This time, I made the decision too late. However, I was never again sent to a survival school.

Chapter 11

∞ May, 1968 Chu Lai ∞

Having survived sea survival school, we took a few days before travelling back to Chu Lai. When I arrived back at the squadron area, I was put on the flight schedule for a late TPQ, or night bombing mission.

Things changed. We were assigned new quarters. I also had a new roommate from Texas. The newbie had been a few months ahead of me in flight school. His name was Captain Pritchard. I could have sworn I saw a guy who looked just like him in Okinawa, his twin?

The new Quonset huts built for us had air-conditioning. What a treat. It made it possible to sleep during any time period, unlike the Southeast Asia huts where sleeping was difficult to impossible during the day and none too pleasant during the night. Flying tired all the time was hard on our aircraft. Small careless mistakes by fatigued pilots were taking their toll on our planes.

I moved my few belongings to the new buildings located on top of a sandy hill. Afterwards, I went down to the beach and spent some time in the warm, turquoise blue water. After a swim, I got ready for another non-remarkable dinner at the mess.

It was 2200 hours. Just as I seemed to close my eyes, the night truck driver on duty, Corporal Heislen, from Pennsylvania, was shaking my shoulder.

"Sir. Sir. Sorry to bother, sir. But it's that time again."

Time to fly. In less than a minute, I had on my flight suit and was in the six by six riding to squadron. I walked into the ready room just after midnight, picked up a mission card and got into my torso harness and G-suit. Signing out an aircraft, I was still half asleep. Get ready, get set, go.

To an outside observer, the night TPQ missions would appear to have been easiest flying of all the missions we flew. Not to mention, the safest. All they ever consisted of was a radar controlled flight from Chu Lai to a target and back the same way. All the time being under radar control and having to fly on instruments from take-off to landing with little chance of having any enemy fire directed at you.

Simple right? But I found the night TPQ missions to be the worst of all we flew.

Because we were under radar control, the missions could be and were flown in all kinds of weather. Since both the spring and summer monsoons had turbulent weather associated with them, it made flying hazardous. Flying TPQs could put you in dangerous thunderstorms requiring adept flying and recovery that daylight close air support missions would not.

During the summer monsoon, a line of thunderstorms would develop a dozen miles inland, move over the ocean in the early evening and dissipate near dawn. When this line was present, it was necessary to penetrate the scud line four times going to and from the target areas we flew. We would take off and immediately penetrate the line to get away from land and out to sea, penetrate it again flying to the target, once more leaving the target, and yet again just before landing.

On one mission in late May, I launched into just such conditions. The overcast was not particularly low, so I made a visual take-off with six, 500 pound bombs. Our normal night load. I turned to the north and penetrated the scud at 1500 feet starting my climb to my assigned altitude. I was focusing on my instruments and the climb schedule of airspeeds and altitudes when I felt a presence in the cockpit that I had not felt before. I was halfway between Chu Lai and Da Nang and was being vectored between storms.

The feeling of the presence overpowered my need to keep my instrument scan going. I looked away from the instrument panel and forward over the nose probe on the right side of the fuselage. The fuselage was glowing blue. My mind disconnected from the hand holding the stick for the next thirty seconds and the plane flew itself. I was mesmerized at the blue glowing wings, the blue tone around the nose and nose probe of the plane and the blue drops of water on my canopy in the boundary layer that did not move.

The plane looked like it was irradiated and I was about to call on the radio to Vice Squad, but was afraid of making a fool of myself. So I flew along for another thirty seconds looking out at the blue glowing light, again the plane on its own without any help from me. I finally did take back the controls and finish the mission, but not before being vectored into the edge of a large turbulent thunderstorm. The plane bounced as it got banged by the vertical air currents.

Making a hard turn out of the storm, I searched for the airstrip to land. Pilots were gathered around talking about what they had just experienced too. Thank God I wasn't alone.

"Did you see it man? The freaking plane was glowing."

"Cobalt blue glowing in the dark."

"So bizarro, dude. I was flipping out."

"Thought I was tripping. So what was it, man?"

"St. Elmo's fire, dude. We just got some St. Elmo's fire."

There were times when I would push the throttle forward when I could only see halfway down the runway, fly into the clouds at 400 feet and stay there the entire mission. The A-4s were reliable for day operations, more so than for night instrument conditions. In the damp climate of Southeast Asia, there were lots of landings that shook the antennas. As did all of the twenty millimeter cannon fire.

On some night missions, I flew when the TACAN, the main navigation instrument, failed. There were other times when the radio failed. Or there were times when the bomb release system left me having to land at night, with three bombs on one wing, no bombs or racks on the other, while having to shoot an instrument approach. Sometimes the plane would not turn right, was nose high and at full right rudder. It's a miracle that as we struck the ground wire and sparks flew that there wasn't just another big ca-boom.

One such mission of the eighty or so that I flew at night was remarkable. Yet again, I was pulled awake in my sandy bed by Corporal Heislen.

"Sir. Sir. Wake up, sir. So sorry to tell ya, sir but your number's up again. Gotta get."

I had two TPQ missions scheduled in the rainy overcast that was prevailing. He took me to the squadron line. I dressed quickly and got my mission card, an 0130 take-off for North Vietnam.

Checking out an airplane, I pre-flighted it and climbed into the A-4's snug cockpit. When I did the check for electrical power, the moustache that I had grown while overseas and the tips of my fingers tingled and shorted out the mike. Small sparks flew when I touched any of the electrical powered devices in the cockpit. I called tower before starting the engine.

"Chu Lai tower this is Dash one. What's the weather out there?"

"Base is overcast at 400 feet. You're clear for take-off."

"Got some sparks flying in the cockpit."

"They all do. Just the storm. Now get that scooter in the air."

"Will do." Despite my concerns, I was required to go ahead with the mission. I started the engine and taxied to the south runway at the far end of the Chu Lai Air Station from our flight line. It was jet black out and the runways and taxiways were shiny black from the light rain.

As I taxied out to the center of the wet black runway, I called Chu Lai departure to get on their frequency.

"Chu Lai, this is Dash one."

"Roger, Dash one. Holding."

I wanted to stay on their frequency just in case something happened immediately after take-off. With this crazy weather, I ran the risk of getting under radar control of Vice Squad, the en-route controller.

It was a minute or two before I got clearance to take-off. In the meantime, I set the lights in the cockpit so they were bright enough that I would have no trouble seeing the instruments. Looking down the runway from the take-off position, I saw nothing but a big, black void. The runway lights disappeared into the gloom at 5,000 to 6,000 feet. The lights from the flight lines of MAG 12 and MAG 13, the Phantom group were dim in the light rain. I was finally given permission to take-off.

"Dash one. You're clear."

"Roger that, Chu Lai."

Easing the throttle to one hundred percent, I started the bumpy roll down the SATS runway. I was accelerating normally without any problem. I was glancing down at my airspeed so that when I reached 150 knots, I could rotate and not risk blowing a tire. Just as I looked down, there was a sudden shuddering of the aircraft and I was being bounced around the cockpit like I wasn't strapped in. I pulled back on the stick to get the nose off the runway. I had blown my nose tire. Damnit.

I jerked on the stick. I had to get the tire up so the plane would accelerate to take-off speed at 155 knots. But it wouldn't accelerate and the nose wouldn't come up.

There was no sense in pulling back on the power. I was staying right at 150 knots. Pulling back the power was going to do little to slow down a fully loaded plane on a wet runway under the rock hard tires.

I could neither get the plane airborne, nor stop the violent shaking, which was only getting worse. I was like a log going down a sluice. Missing the first arresting gear, I was starting to drift left and couldn't control it, so I slammed down the arresting hook. As I did so, the plane immediately went into the midfield MOREST, taking the wire off center and rolling out to a stop with my nose fishtailing to the right. Smack. Into the bunkers I went. Just like what had happened to the dead pilot I had replaced. No!

I rode back to the flight line on a crash truck. Just as I got off the truck, immediately when I arrived, I was handed another yellow mission card.

I couldn't believe it.

"No time to fret, Lieutenant. Get your butt back out there," the mission commander barked.

I signed it off, got another plane and taxied out to the jet black runway just like I had done twenty minutes before. When I got to the take-off end of the runway, they were still getting my previous scooter off. It had taken all of the energy and will I had to walk out to the second aircraft after nearly wiping out the one before.

When departure gave me clearance to take-off, I pushed the throttle forward and as I did so, lifted off at a point just before the location of the tow truck and crash trucks that were still towing my other aircraft from the taxiway to our flight line.

I was over an hour late when I landed from that mission. Walking into the ready room, I was ready for a beer, but instead got another mission card.

"Look, I'm flat out. I don't wanna do this one."

"You've been through the ringer tonight. I get 'cha." The duty officer picked up the phone to call group. "The scud's thick. This next one's gonna be so late. Pilot's requesting to cancel, sir."

"Request denied, Lieutenant." The group duty officer barked. "And what's the name of the pilot that was gonna bail?"

"I'll check," the duty officer gave me a look.

I shook my hand at my throat, pleading for him to not rat me out. Thankfully he nodded.

"No one in particular, sir. Just a general request."

"Well, that's a damned good thing. We'd better not have one damned Marine that ain't got the intestinal fortitude to fly under these conditions. Ya got that?" he roared into the phone loud enough for us both to hear.

I got so angry. I just took the mission card, checked out another plane, stalked out to the flight line and took off. When I returned, the first light of day was showing over the horizon. As I rode up to the debriefing shack at air intelligence to debrief, I found I could remember nothing of the mission I had just flown. Massive fatigue had set in. Thankfully, I had the coordinates on my mission sheet from my kneeboard.

After taking a shower, I lay down in the sunlight that penetrated the green window of the Quonset hut and tried to keep my eyes open, but found it impossible to do so. My head was churning with thoughts about a pilot flying under just such conditions as I had flown the night before. He had taken the arresting gear the wrong way, just a few weeks before, doing considerable damage to an aircraft.

Flying at night was exhausting because there were too many things required to complete during the day. Not to mention that simply flying was tiring in nature. Just as I was drifting off to sleep, Captain Pritchard was returning.

"Gotta love them TPQs. Every time I get back to the hooch, I meet myself walking out again."

That was a good way to put it. Flying TPQs was a different experience when the weather was good, but still they were no fun. Perhaps one half of those I flew were, in some degree or another, under visual or semi-visual conditions. But I was better off than most.

With the background I had flying tactically during the day and having intelligence reports of action off over at I Corps, I was in a position, when flying up and down just off the coast at night, to see the full panorama of the war. I generally knew what was happening.

Night after night, I would be pulled awake by Heislen to ride down to the flight line. The moon lit the west field where the Army had their choppers. There was a POW camp at the intersection of the road and the west field runway with an access road. It was surrounded by gorgeous sandy beaches that were open around the Chu Lai area. Tempering the beauty, however, was the constant pop and orange light of the flares and the tracers on the perimeter.

Chapter 12

More and more, I was flying TPQs. Luck of the draw, I guess. Each night as I got to the squadron area, I would check to see who was flying that night. The assignments were written out in grease pencil on the board where the flight schedule was posted.

The tension wasn't as great when we didn't have to fly instruments because we didn't need clearances. When we did fly instruments, as long as we didn't have problems with failure of the ones we needed, we could fly the missions faster.

Had I not been so tired all the time, I might have enjoyed flying the TPQs, because I loved flying the scooter. But the mood changed when everything was a crisis or needed total concentration to be successful.

Most pilots enjoyed the nighttime TPQs and thought they were walks in the park. But not me. I had become more claustrophobic in the cockpit at night. Never a good thing. I felt terror.

We flew radar missions ordered from the controllers at Chu Lai, Da Nang, Hue/Phu Bair, Dong Ha, which was just south of the DMZ and Khe Sanh until it was abandoned in May. We even flew via an Air Force Controller. Khe Sanh, "Milky," the Air Force Controller and Don Ha radar would run our aircraft into North Vietnam. None of the others would do so.

During the time Khe Sanh was under siege, the majority of the missions we flew were sent there. I was glad to see us abandon that base because the 2,000 Marines trapped there couldn't conduct operations. We were sending an inordinate number of our aircraft there and were not supporting other units in contact.

On some of my night missions during good weather, I would pre-flight the aircraft, make a rapid start, do all the checks and try to get airborne rapidly to meet the flight schedule. When we flew with the Chu Lai radar controller, the missions were so short that if we didn't log taxi time, they probably wouldn't have qualified as a flight. It was more like going around after being waved off on a carrier landing.

When flying at Chu Lai with their controller, I would take off, make a hard turn out to sea, another turn over the sea, roll wings level and get the controller, who would follow us on take-off to quickly get me on line to the target. I wanted to drop the bombs, dump enough fuel to land safely, drop the gear and be done. It was possible to fly a mission to the Chu Lai radar controller and log flight time in less than twenty minutes.

Over time, the missions seemed to start running together. Typically we would fly up the coast to the northern part of I Corps, near the DMZ. We would be under the control of Vice Squad until we got near the ASRAT radar site and then be turned over to the ground controller.

He would give us a turn for identification and then put us on a radar vector, calling out the meters to target. He had to keep within narrow margins of airspeed and altitude. When within 5,000 meters of target, he would have us arm the bombs and fly until he gave us a signal. At 'mark-mark' we would release the bombs.

Although usually at altitudes of 10,000 feet or more, the bright white flash of the bombs would be visible to us in the cockpit. North Vietnam was a black void at night.

There were no lights anywhere. South Vietnam had lights in the cities, the larger villages and over the ocean. Fishermen fished in small round boats the size of an old wash tub and each had a light. Under certain conditions, the ocean and the sky looked the same. Vertigo was a possibility if you didn't keep scanning your instruments or watching the coastline.

Even during visual radar missions, there could be moments of excitement. One evening, I was flying at 11,000 feet over North Vietnam on a vector from Dong Ha. I was ten or fifteen miles north of the DMZ when I caught the glimmer of a light in my canopy. I looked at my instruments to see if my generator was going out, as that was a common symptom. I saw nothing wrong.

Suddenly, I realized that I was being perfectly tracked by explosions from a radar controlled or visually controlled fifty-seven millimeter gun or larger. Then I realized why he was following me so easily. I had all my lights on.

I had forgotten to turn them off when I left South Vietnam. I flipped off the master light switch and made a hard turn toward the South China Sea. The orange balls of flame passed through the position I would have been at just after I turned. That was too close for comfort.

When the North Vietnamese opened up with ground fire at night, it was not piecemeal. It was occasionally possible to see a photo plane, usually an F-8 from the Navy, or a Phantom from the Air Force flying a photo line. They were marked by extremely bright flashes, one after the other like a continuous dotted line of fire. It would trigger all the guns in sight and thousands of them would be shooting at the straight line of fireballs as they came south.

Completing the missions over North Vietnam and flying back to Chu Lai along the coast visually gave me a chance to just watch the war. On the best nights, it was possible to just see

Chu Lai, one half hour to the south and 140 miles away and everything else in between that was lit up.

There were usually airstrikes visible in Laos. Others in South Vietnam. You could tell where they were since it was possible to see virtually all of I Corps on clear nights from 12,000 feet over Da Nang. By comparing the light from the cities and bases to the location of the flares and bright flashes of the bombs, it was possible to see most of the airborne action from the coast as you travelled down it.

The most destructive and impressive thing I saw on one of my flights down the white coast, occurred at 0200 hours after I had just departed the DMZ. I was two or three miles off shore and watching my instrument panel when it got as light as day.

For a moment, I thought the sun was rising. I looked landward over the canopy rail, and sure enough, the sun was coming right out of the ground. A giant bright white and orange ball was five miles inland and appeared to be the sun rising from the valley between the coastal plain and the A Shau Valley. But it wasn't the sun at all.

"Vice Squad, this is Hellborne two four dash one. Over."

"Maintain radio silence, Hellborne two four."

"Roger that."

As I continued to fly down along the coast, I wondered what was going on. When I landed, I reported what I saw, but it never showed up in any intelligence reports. However, I heard from an Army pilot that 144 Army helicopters brought into the country by a new unit had been parked together instead of separated or put in revetments. A Viet Cong sapper unit had been able to penetrate the defense and got them burning. After getting a few burning, the rest followed. A massive explosion and fire ensued.

The war from the air and from the ground were two very different things. The ground war was violent and massive. There were two and one half Marine Divisions, two Army

Divisions, ARVN units, and hundreds of aircraft fighting in an area that averaged forty miles in width and was only 140 miles long. At night, on certain occasions, it was possible to see the aircraft expending their ordnance. As well as the ships on the coast firing inland, artillery being fired here and there and ground units in contact with flares marking their position. At any given time, there may have been 300,000 combatants in that compact 600 square mile area.

Chapter 13

∞ June 9, 1968 ∞

Acouple of months after I arrived at Chu Lai, most officer's Quonset huts were outfitted with air conditioners so that as pilots, we could escape the sweltering heat and get some sleep. Day after day we watched water dripping from the unit. Being the enterprising make-shift lot that we were, an ammo can was procured to collect the runoff. Someone even rigged up a shower hose. What sweet relief. From then on, our air conditioner became our source of 'fresh' water. No more stiff flight suits.

I was scheduled for two preplanned missions, the first one with an 1100 take-off. Major Tom Lewis was going to be the flight leader and I would be on his wing.

Freshly showered, I walked the 200 meters from my Quonset hut to the briefing room and met Major Lewis. He was five foot nine and had a red crew cut. We briefed for the mission and caught a ride down to the squadron area. It was overcast over the land, but clear over the sea.

Launching off the north runway, we were bound toward the Hue/Phu Bai area. As we approached the city of Hoi An, we were called by Vice Quad and given an emergency divert to cover RESCAP of a downed pilot in the A Shau Valley.

We switched frequency to get on the same channel as the RESCAP and heard them talking about the downed plane.

"Confirmed. A-4 scooter. Shot down by a SAM. See if you can get a visual."

"Visual confirmed. At your one o'clock in the meadow. Still attached to his chute."

His wingman had just rolled out of the area. We were returned to Vice Squad to fly our assigned mission, because no rescue aircraft or controller was available to save him. I felt terrible leaving him there.

We flew our mission, returned to Chu Lai and landed. No sooner had we set down, we were told to hurry up and turn around we would be going right back out. To the same RES-CAP.

It took a quarter of an hour for us to find out the details and launch again. Time was survival. The longer you were on the ground, the less chance you had of being rescued. The pilot was a Marine from VMA-121. He was a captain, Roy Schmidt, who had been in the flight class I took at Meridian, Mississippi in May of 1966. He was shot down on the Laos side of the A Shau Valley. The meadow was a clearing near the Ho Chi Minh trail.

Grabbing a sandwich, as my blood sugar felt like it was about twenty, we re-launched again to the north. This time, we went directly to a point just east of the mountains west of Da Nang and switched our frequency. Red Crown was the airborne rescue coordinator who flew into areas of downed aircraft and coordinated the RESCAP.

We could tell things were not going well before we checked in. There were aircraft rolling in on the flak suppression calling to their flight controllers about the heavy ground fire.

A Jolly Green Giant which was a large, single rotor helicop-ter was trying to help. But it spun into the ground and crashed, having been shot down. As we approached target, we could see it burst into flames taking the whole crew with it. A second Jolly

Green was orbiting five miles west of the downed pilot. As the second helo going in, he reported that he was taking heavy ground fire.

Our flight split up so that we could each analyze the situation independently. I dropped back and looked down to see if I could tell where the pilot was, where the ground fire was coming from and where the rescue helo could land. It didn't take long to determine the situation.

The pilot, Captain Schmidt, could be seen in the meadow. The clearing was above a road that led from the floor of the A Shau Valley to the Ho Chi Minh trail. It was possible to see the parachute in the middle of the clearing, some fifteen or twenty yards from the tree line between the road and the valley floor. The remaining Jolly Green continued to orbit the area and was now over Laos. The ground fire went in as far as I could see, in almost every possible direction. I didn't see how anything could keep from getting hit anywhere within sight.

Red Crown continued to attempt coordinating the aircraft trying to suppress the anti-aircraft fire. But nothing short of a nuclear explosion would have cleared what I was seeing.

"My bird's taken so many hits. I dunno how much longer I can hang in," reported the second Jolly Green pilot.

"Roger that," answered Red Crown.

I held my A-4 in orbit at 10,000 feet as two Phantoms from the Air Force rolled in and dropped west of the position of the parachute and Jolly Green. Despite their strafing, they didn't even make a dent in the amount of ground fire going off in that area.

Not only were there small arms firing, there were the big guns. Ones more typically seen north near Tchepone or in North Vietnam. I couldn't believe there were that many guns in all of South Vietnam. Especially of that size. I wondered how many thousands of troops had to be in that A Shau area to cover the geography, which was intrinsically my visual scope in every direction. According to intelligence reports there weren't supposed to be this many weapons.

Our time was up. There was only one flight ahead of us. The controller at Red Crown had given up on the RESCAP because there were no planes behind us.

"I'm hit. Hit bad. I'm going down," the pilot cried out from the Jolly Green.

"God damn it. Another one," muttered Red Crown.

As he took up a heading toward Khe Sanh, we rolled in to take out whatever we could. The parachute could still be seen in the meadow.

The lead, Major Lewis, rolled in and I followed. We didn't need much accuracy. I followed him down as he shot his load of Zuni five inch rockets into the overall pattern of flashes that were covering the face of the ground before us. I then salvoed mine just to the right of his, running south.

He pulled up and I kept going down, just above the valley floor, at more than 500 knots. As I skimmed the ground, I looked up and saw him above me at 6,000 or 8,000 feet. Pulling up into a steep climb, I joined him over the mountains to the west as we cleared the area and went back to Vice Squad for return to the base.

My stomach was sickened leaving a comrade down, having no ability to rescue him. Especially one that I knew. But I just couldn't bear to think about it and instead focused on simply flying the damn plane.

We flew straight out to sea, then down the coast. As we did so, we heard over the radio that indeed the entire RESCAP was terminated. Poor Roy had no chance of being rescued from the time he was shot down.

After landing, I checked over the plane, certain I would find holes somewhere, but was surprised that I did not. Major Lewis walked over to me and shook his head.

"How is it possible to fly through so much fire at the altitudes we were at and not get hit?"

"I dunno, sir. I just don't know. Kinda amazed myself."

I returned to the living quarters and took a shower. There was a note that had been left on the bed from the American Red Cross. No one wants to see those. Most times it means a family emergency. But in my case, I found out that I now had another child. Two boys now, instead of one.

"Well, I'll be. I have another son."

Although I was happy and elated that all had gone well with the birth, as far as I knew, nothing would replace the twinge in your heart knowing that due to some meaningless war, you weren't present for your own child's birth. I went to the USO club. I should celebrate, right?

"A round of champagne for everyone. I'm a dad, again. My wife just gave birth to a son," I waved the American Red Cross telegram.

"Congrats, Marine," the bewitching manager of the club said giving me a hug. She handed me some cigars to pass around. "Isn't it also your birthday today?"

"Yep, sure is."

"I thought so. We baked you a cake, Gene."

"And it's some good chit!" Galchick, one of the flight line crew mechanics called out. "Glad you finally made it, sir. We were gonna dig in without 'cha," he laughed with his arm looped around one of the USO gals.

I had made friends with many of the gals from the USO. It felt nice just to hear a female voice once in a while. Most of them were young girls, just out of college. I watched over many of them and made sure they stayed out of trouble for the most part. They were naïve twenty-somethings and ill-prepared to see the gore of war firsthand.

Even though we all drank together in the same USO, the enlisted guys mostly kept to themselves. They played cards or dominos or wore out the pinball machines that lined the walls. But we were all comrades. As pilots we owed them. They kept our planes safely in the air. Sometimes cannibalizing leftover parts from a scrapped plane to replace in another. They were a vital part of VMA-311 too. I took a seat next to Corporal Galchick.

"Thanks for the champers and congrats on the baby, sir."

"Happy to oblige, Corporal. It really sucks not to be there."

"I'm sure. War sucks, sir."

We took swigs of the bubbly cheap champagne. Its bitter taste matched my mood. I had a lot on my mind.

"Intel's reporting Captain Roy Schmidt MIA. From the Jolly Green crash landing in that minefield near Khe Sanh."

"Crappers. Not another one," the tech scoffed. "Another one down and never to be heard of again. It's bullshit man."

"Yeah."

"We worry about you guys when we strap ya in," he revealed.

"Do ya?"

"Yeah. I was the one working on the scooter of Chuck Porterfield. Had him loaded with a shitload of explosives and napalm. The bird's wheels caught fire on the takeoff rollout."

"No joke? That's how it happened?"

"Yeah. He missed the arresting gear at the end of the run way and went airborne. He ejected, but came down right on top of his exploding ordnance. It was awful."

"I can imagine," I was moved by this young man sharing his painful story.

"It's a tough one for me. Can't stop thinking about it," he said taking another drink. "Cuz I strapped him in and launched him."

I put my hand on the tech's shoulder and ordered another round. So much responsibility and pressure was put on these men barely out of their teens.

"Can't help but wonder. Is there was something I missed on the pre-launch check? Something that may have caused the landing gears to catch fire?" There were tears in his eyes which he quickly wiped away.

"Don't beat yourself up, Marine," I patted him on the back. "We all do only what we can. We fly tin rockets. Accidents happen."

"Thanks, sir. He was a good pilot."

Nine months after this incident, the Marines sent a battalion into the A Shau Valley. They were the same troops that had been at Khe Sanh during the siege, which had just been lifted. Once the Marines moved in, they took out many of the snipers. They occupied the full area of gunfire that I had just seen.

But for Roy, that was too late. I took a new look at how ineffective we were in destroying the enemy. Downing the rest of the champagne in one gulp, I headed for the bar and ordered a double bourbon straight up. Happy Birthday to me.

Chapter 14

I knew from the first week in Chu Lai that I was different from most of the other pilots. The 'devil-may-care, tomor-row-we-may-die' attitude, that I once had too, was long gone. The other attack pilots still were generally that way.

They laughed more than I did, were more open and friendly and seemed to take things less seriously than I thought they should. What seemed unreal to them, seemed very real to me. I was keenly aware of what was happening on the perimeter and what the intelligence reports from Americal said.

Americal was the name given to the 23rd Infantry Division of the US Army. Most divisions had numbers, but the term Americal stemmed from coining America and New Caledonia, which was duty during WWII when the division fought to keep Japanese forces out of New Caledonia. I kept up a map showing where battles were and actions. I sensed a reality in the war that my fellow pilots seemingly did not.

I was different from them in all aspects of dealing with the war. I didn't have any emotions about the things we did, but I didn't think they were funny either. I never laughed at their crass jokes about things. I realized, however, that their warped sense of humor was more of a coping mechanism to defer what they actually had to face every day more than anything else.

Many of them were oblivious to what was going on with guerilla warfare just outside the walls of the base. When I first realized how close we were to invasion by nearby Viet Cong in the village, I took precautions. Assigned to be a platoon commander, I checked out the proper weapons and equipment in case of an attack. If under siege, we were to form into infantry units to defend the base. I wanted to be ready. I spoke to the base perimeter commander and kept myself briefed about the conditions around the base.

It was eye-opening to realize what was happening just a few hundred meters from where we lived. An attack could occur on short notice. It irked me that I seemed to be more concerned than my fellow officers.

It was a big surprise to all when Major Reisner, the perimeter commander to whom I had spoken, was captured. But after what he had revealed, it wasn't any surprise to me at all.

I was never sure if the internalized anxiety I felt was the reason I couldn't relate to many of my fellow aviators in the squadron. During briefs and in the ready room, I took on my missions without alarm. But I sensed their underlying anxiety. They never spoke about it, but fear of the unknown was there. It was buried deep.

Up to the point that I rolled in on a target, time seemed to stop. I was focused solely on the target. I saw no ground fire when the target was in focus, unless it occurred at some point after or before I was on the run in. The targets seemed so big, so easy to hit and so defined that I wondered how others could miss. Over time, I came to understand that I was reacting to fear in a different way than they were. But who knows, maybe they simply had no fear and I did. Men were not encouraged to speak about such things. This was war.

The only time I ever felt any real fear was when I walked out at night for a TPQ mission in bad weather. It was not fear of combat missions, but of the claustrophobic conditions of the

A-4's snug cockpit. Our Marine scooters were hand-me-downs from the Navy. God only knows what problems could occur with their parts and instruments; and often did in the weather.

It was not until years later that I thought about something that continually happened, but at the moment didn't realize. Over time, I saw other pilots change and become more like me. It was a revelation.

From my very first days in Vietnam, I was conscious of the continual emissions of fire. Flares. The shitters burning. The fires around the base when planes crashed. Fuel burning. Objects burned after being hit by incoming rockets or mortar. Those sights and the acrid burning smells bothered me from the moment I got into the country. It brought me back to that time in my young life. The fire. The smoke. It shook me to the core. I knew my fear was based on what could happen when caught in such circumstances, unable to escape a fire. Just like the burning crash I had experienced prior to my tour in Vietnam. My other fellow pilots were not operating from that perspective, having never experienced those sensations.

Depending on one's previous experiences, a jet aircraft could be viewed in more than one way. I had always valued them as marvelous works of engineering that allowed one to experience the emotional highs and exhilaration of flight in its extremes. Flying aerobatic maneuvers. Barely skimming the ground at high speeds. One adrenalin rush after another, just by being in such conditions. Even when seeing them flown by someone else.

But if you saw flight from the perspective of the World War II bomber pilots, your viewpoint might be different. I heard the stories from the WWII pilots who flew in the worst conditions of attack and dogfighting. I kept my feelings in check, but maybe the younger pilots with their seemingly aloof egos and humor were expressing in words what I felt from within.

The pilot of a jet powered fighter bomber, in combat, is flying nothing more than a blow torch in a flying fuel tank, loaded with explosives. A pilot's attitude depends on his experiences and my experiences left me with the unexploded bomb perspective more than was healthy.

After months of flying these missions, I began to see the younger pilots' attitudes change. One at a time, the probability of an incident occurring turned into the reality of it happening and it was changing them to be more like me.

The first pilot to do so actually revealed that fear during a conversation as I arrived at the squadron. He had been shot down at night, just south of Da Nang and wasn't rescued until morning. He was no longer on the night flight schedule for either radar or close air support missions.

During the time I flew with the three squadrons to which I was assigned, I saw fifteen or more of my fellow pilots, that I flew with daily, shot down in attacks on the enemy. Each time an incident happened, I noticed how my peers got a hard line in their jaw. Their eyes didn't laugh anymore. They didn't join in the light banter about things that were not light. They withdrew from the conversations and were, in one way or another, on the sidelines.

Reality had replaced probability of the bad things that could and did happen to them. They found out how serious these endless missions really were. But worse, they experienced fear to the core. And that fear, permanently changed them. It didn't seem to affect them in the cockpit, but it did affect how they acted and now reacted to things on the ground. I was still their wingman and lead on many occasions. I felt they flew as well as before, but were now conditioned to see things from a different, more guarded perspective.

When pilots were shot down, their condition was not known for quite some time. No one could tell you what had become of them. When the duty officer, who kept up the flight schedule, got a call from group that we had a plane down, he would mark it on the board. When the rest of us found the pilot was rescued, the information would be given to the other pilots in the ready room. But when one was killed, captured, or MIA, the name was just erased and the person ceased to exist.

There really wasn't anything that could be said. It took some time for the facts to get to the squadron and the effect would vary from one person to another. When I replaced the pilot, Captain Chuck Porterfield, who I now knew had been killed when he ran off the end of the runway, I found out nothing about him except his name. That is until the avionics tech told me. Because none of the other pilots talked about him at all. This was the effect of war.

Chapter 15

The General. I'll never forget this story. We didn't get many missions to support helicopter operations. During the first part of the Vietnam conflict, circa 1965 and 1966, they were fairly common. The first time I saw someone die unnecessarily really shook me up.

It was during one of the few support operations for an infantry insertion on a ridge seaward from Hue/Phu Bai. There was now a Marine Air Station there. This particular incident was witnessed by dozens of other pilots. But due to the rank of the individual involved, most of them remained silent on the radio. All of them agreed, they would not have managed the incident the same way, nor done the same thing. Had I been on the radio frequency, I would have said something, regardless of rank, to the aircrew just to save a life.

Two of our A-4 Skyhawks were armed with forward firing guns and rockets. On this particular day, typical of coordinated infantry helo operations, the mission was behind schedule. Since we had limited fuel, only one and a half hours after take-off, we were orbiting at 10,000 feet at 220 knots, which was maximum conservation airspeed, whilst the operation was developing.

It was late in the morning and I was leading the flight. We were watching the operation, ready to roll in at a moment's notice, if necessary. The anxiety of watching one CH-46 after another go into the zone, ground pounding Marines disembarking onto the ridge and the helos departing continually kept us alert.

I had seen such operations when helos inserted and retracted teams before. The teams on the ground would call the CH-46 or Huey into the zone, whispering that there was no enemy. Then they watched helplessly as the chopper flew into heavy ground fire from guerillas on approach to land or during departure from the zones. Since it was at that point we were required to roll in, we were kept alert no matter what we were doing, just in case the CH-46s needed our backup.

Because this operation was delayed, we had to stay higher and fly slower, putting us in a poor position to attack. We were more of a moral support factor, in my opinion, because of our fuel limitations than a direct support. There had not yet been a need to roll in, but there were times when the NVA would let some of the troops get on the ground and then open up on the choppers incessantly when the unit was split. They were trying to prevent the rest of the unit from supporting those who were already on the ground.

While watching the continuing operations, our flight was monitoring Guard frequency, the universal emergency frequency used to transmit when in a crisis. In the areas we were flying in, it was also used to transmit all manner of instructions and warnings. Such that most of the time, when in the target area, it was necessary to turn off the frequency to be able to conduct missions. That was not the case on this mission.

While watching the second wave of ground troops come in, a Mayday came over Guard from an Air Force RF-4, a photo reconnaissance plane from well up in Laos. It had taken some ground fire and was coming into South Vietnam to try to get away from the Laotian border, where capture was certain if they were shot down.

Instead of going to another frequency, the RF-4 Phantom stayed on Guard with a continuous relay of information to other aircraft in the area who were vectoring in to help them if they could. I had to turn off my emergency frequency so that I was able to maintain contact with my own mission. Occasionally, I would turn back to Guard when I could, since we had the ordnance to cover a RESCAP, knew the bases available for Air Force pilot under siege to land, and additionally, had experience bringing in wingmen with battle damage to bases before.

As the injured bird came down into South Vietnam, I could tell by listening that something was different. The pilot was being deferred to by the other Air Force planes. He kept up his running commentary on Guard. As such, I could only follow part of what was going on. He was now in South Vietnam.

I was off Guard for my mission for about two or three minutes. When I came back up, the pilot had decided to land on the beach. He still must have had some altitude because he kept talking for some time. I didn't know where he was and what beach he was talking about because of the need to turn off the channel and because he was already being escorted by someone.

When I heard he was going to try to land on the beach, I wanted to come up on frequency and guide the crew. But I had no idea where the plane was, what condition it was in and if it was being escorted by someone who knew I Corps as well as I did. I was running low on fuel, so I departed the area, switching on Guard again after I had talked to my wingman.

I had seen half a dozen planes after they ditched. The biggest piece of any of them left afterward was a tail, burned way beyond recognition. Although these aircraft were not F-4s, they were structurally just as strong.

By the time I turned back on Guard, the plane in trouble crashed and was destroyed with one crewman ejecting. Upon landing, I found out that the plane crashed within just a few miles of where we were orbiting, barely away from the

Hue/Phu Bai Air Station. More significant, the pilot was an Air Force General. He was killed on impact.

Not knowing the details until reviewing later intelligence reports, I cannot say for certain that I could have prevented his death. But unlike the General, I would never ride in a jet if I didn't know how to eject. And I would certainly never have bypassed the runways he did.

I had seen older pilots killed several times doing just this. A jet aircraft is different than the older propeller driven fighters. Props have the fuel in the wings, the moving parts of the engine at high temperature are enclosed in an engine block and the engine sits ahead of them. They carried much less fuel.

A jet aircraft is constructed differently. That is why they put ejection seats in them. In a jet, the pilot sits in front of the engine. The engine has vanes in it that come apart and fly through the fuselage at 450 degrees centigrade or more. The fuselage and wings are all filled with fuel, hydraulic fluid, and internal parts of the aircraft's flight control system. When the plane hits anything, it starts to come apart and the engine will likely come forward, with the vanes coming through the fuel tanks.

I was not on frequency long enough to stop what appeared to be the useless death of the Air Force General, as the pilot turned out to be. His co-pilot, in ejecting, made the better decision. Since all the aircraft airborne for 200 miles in every direction heard this happen, and ejecting was mandatory procedure under such conditions, I am left to wonder if he died because he was a General and no one would contradict his decision. That or the chase plane told him not to ride it in and he did so anyway, defying more modern principles of jet flying.

People I knew and some I did not know were being killed every day. Seeing someone killed so uselessly, when it should not have happened, affected me more than the combat casualties. Especially when, like in this situation, the tragedy was seen by so many who knew the correct procedure to follow, yet said nothing. Not even the co-pilot. In this case, no one took the initiative to prevent it from happening. Just so tragic. I simply didn't understand. Why hadn't they said anything? Was rank and protocol worth more than life?

Chapter 16

∞ Summer, 1968 ∞

By the middle of June, 1968, I had flown enough missions to be a section leader in combat. Occasionally, I'd pick up the briefing for a flight and meet the wingman at the squadron area. I was experiencing, for the first time, the command structure in the air wing. It varied from the ground forces for which I had my initial training.

In the ground forces, an officer's rank defined command, but in the air, it did not. Ground rank was superseded by experience and recent qualifications. The rank started with wingman, went to section leader in command of two aircraft, division leader in command of four aircraft and up. I was not in the habit of telling Lt. Colonels and Colonels what to do, but when airborne, I was doing so when the group pilots came to fly who were not section leaders. I was in that situation as I waited on the road near the briefing shack for a ride to the squadron area.

I always wondered why the U.S. Army could have privates riding around in their own jeeps and yet we had only one six by six for over 150 marine pilots and had to often find our own way to our missions. Go figure. I was picked up for this mission by someone who wondered the same thing.

Today, I was picked up by a Navy jeep, one not seen often at Chu Lai. It was being driven by a Chief Petty Officer. Since I thought that the only Navy personnel on the base were medical folks, I was curious as to what he was doing there. After the obligatory salutes, I asked him.

"So, how is it that a Navy Petty Officer is picking me up?"

"You're on my way. To a Seabee pickup."

"Oh?" I queried.

"Yessir. With a reserve unit outta Boston."

"Accent noted," and we both laughed.

"We work the base water system. Fix the roads. And unload the ships and stuff. So what do you do, Sir?"

"I often wonder," and we both laughed again. "I fly the Scooter."

"Oh yeah, the A-4. The one we see out there scraping those metal hooks with sparks flying on the runway."

"Yeah, we land with our hooks down on the arresting gear."

"Damn. Sparks and all. So whatcha got going today, if you don't mind my asking?" he tentatively questioned. "Gonna bomb some gooks?" and he cleared his throat. "Sir?"

"Nope. Today I'm meeting a full Colonel, the base commander, to fly a combat mission north of the Da Nang area."

"No, shit. Sir. Uhh . . sorry for my French."

"No problem." I was used to the colorful language frequented more so by the enlisted.

"So what's the deal with yous guys getting to da flight lines?"

"We catch whatever rides we can." To put myself on his level I used language he related to. "It sucks. The whole transportation issue is a debacle."

"I hear ya, sir. Pickin' yous up means I'm late for my other rendezvous. But I'm happy to oblige, sir."

"Thanks. You saved another layer of my boots," we both laughed. The tarmac was about 110 degrees.

"We're both slaves to Americal," I offered.

"Yessirree. The Army's got our balls, sir."

Both the Marines and the Navy relied on the Army for food supplies, which were brought in by Navy ships. Oddly, delivered by no one in some areas. My roommate, captain Pritchard, had been eyeing a flight suit that was drying on the line for several days. He only had one and hoped it dried out before being called up for another mission. I had one, also, and one with the side torn out of it.

"Heck, my t-shirts and drawers are threadbare from God only knows what lye soaps are used by the Vietnamese laundry."

"Yep, sir. I hear ya."

"After one mission, my flight suit smelled so bad. But I'll be damned if I was gonna let it get ate up by whatever shit they use to wash it."

"That's a damn shame, Sir."

"Yeah, we've taken to siphoning off water from the condenser on our air con. Saving it in ammunition tins. And then using that water to wash was we need."

"That's just so wrong, Sir."

I sighed, thinking about how much we must have stunk. I was sure our cockpits were rank too.

"Hard to live with yourself wearing such smelly gear. Worse than being in the bush."

"You're a nice guy, sir. I'll see what I can do for ya."

He dropped me off at the squadron. He asked that I write down a list of what we needed. By the time I got back from the debrief of the mission, I found a gross of boxed shorts, a gross of t-shirts, fifty or more sheets, light globes, paint and the address of the Seabee unit in case we needed anything else.

"Holy, shit Lathrop," called out one of my bunkmates. "Who'd you have to do to get us all this crap?"

"Whaddaya mean?"

"Take a look at your bunk," the officer pointed.

"Well, I'll be." On top of my bunk, in new plastic wrap, were two brand new Navy Nomex flight suits. I had just been introduced to the Marine Corps Supply System. I had heard about it all along. It operated continually at all levels and was scroungery at the highest level of proficiency. But I didn't care. For once, I wouldn't stink.

But supplies weren't the only challenge faced by the Marines. As we flew mission after mission and lost planes, they were replaced with ones the Navy didn't want. When they left Yankee Station cruise complete, their planes, which had endured hundreds of carrier landings and recent combat missions, were transferred to the Marines. Each shipment was somewhat different, a newer version of the Scooter.

As soon as they arrived, we painted over the Navy markings, the Navy names on the cockpit rails and flew them. The dark gray paint over the letters did not totally hide what was written. Even if the planes were not in the full bloom of youth and would certainly not have been featured in any military air show, they fit our needs. Thus, Navy hand-me-downs filled Marine revetments and kept us flying.

As these replacement aircraft came in, cockpit configurations started showing up with new modifications that we had not seen before. Switches that had on/off modifications for weapons we did not carry had been put in them. Different engine and fuselage modifications made every flight a challenge. But a flight was a flight. A mission a mission. Those planes met the mission requirements and the Marines, well, we just made it work. Anything to keep flying.

After my black market experience with the CPO and the recent aircraft replacement, I had a better understanding of how things matriculated through the system. I planned to educate myself further.

Six by sixes and jeeps started showing up with Marine Corps numbers that I had not seen before. Some were of makes that the Marine Corps did not have. I found out how the supply and demand system really worked.

Someone would get a case of bourbon from the mess or from the Army. Booze was the unit of exchange at the Army wrecking yard. In one case, the NCOIC accepted a case of bourbon for two damaged six by sixes. One got hit by a mine under the front wheels and the other had been hit with one under the back wheels. Marines put them together and now we had one six by six. The same was true of the jeeps. We would paint USMC numbers on the equipment and they would be ours for a period of time until the U.S. Army made an inspection of our area, checked the engine numbers against their records, and retrieved their equipment, which we had restored.

This ingenuity in restoring broken down equipment extended beyond the Marine Corps at times. A Navy A-4 landed in the arresting gear and destroyed the forward part of the aircraft when it had a front landing gear fail on landing. Shortly afterwards, an A-4 from another ship landed that had its aft destroyed by an oxygen fire and could not land on its carrier, so it landed at Chu Lai. The Navy had struck two aircraft. Our crafty Marine Corps maintenance crew disconnected the aft part of one and replaced it with the forward part of the other. As such, a pilot flew it back to one of the carriers, with the front numbers on the aircraft from his carrier and the aft number from another.

Through my black market Seabee connection, I obtained flight suits, underclothes and other items for my personnel's use. I also started collecting weapons and other registered artillery items, all thanks to the U.S. Army. We would be prepared.

Part of my intel job involved investigations. Anything that caused an injury, or loss of any kind had to be investigated. Since we were experiencing constant injuries and losses, investigations of all kinds were assigned to the officers in their spare time. And spare time or not, the investigations got done.

My first investigation was done after one Marine had shot another accidentally when loading a .45 pistol. In examining the situation, I found the pistol to be stolen from the U.S. Army. I was unable to return it because the system they used to keep track of weapons was not accessible at our base, despite being the headquarters of the Americal Division.

As a result, I ended up with the weapon, which was going to be used if legal action were taken against the sergeant who fired it accidentally. I had to keep it with me to maintain the chain of evidence. Without wishing to do so, I had acquired a gun which was now my responsibility and no one else's. I found a holster, put my .38 in the emergency flight vest we wore if shot down and carried the .45 until I left Vietnam.

I handled several of those investigations. When I could not return the weapons to the Marines, in order to maintain the chain of evidence, I had to keep them locked up myself. I was able to turn in the M-16 I had checked out if called on to lead a platoon. And instead, use one I had confiscated, a U.S. Army rifle that I kept locked in my quarters. Most of the items I had were weapons from the Army. I never determined where they came from. But I was happy to have them.

Chapter 17

∞ July, 1968 ∞

During the summer of 1968, we flew and flew and flew more. It did not seem to ever stop. We climbed out of one cockpit and into another. We saw sunsets and sunrises day after day. Time as we had known it before had little meaning. Under the conditions we were operating in, it seemed to have no meaning at all.

A day on the flight line is defined by that period between midnight and midnight the following day. That concept had no meaning under the conditions of continual missions that prevailed. It was possible to fly at 0800 and 1100, stand the duty from 1800 to midnight, fly at 0200 and 0500 thus flying four separate missions in a day. Flying all those missions and still being required to stand duty was insanity. We would log only two for that day, yet really we had flown four in twenty-four hours.

With all the flying, the duty, the intelligence work and extra details, sleep started to be left out. I could only catch a wink or two during short periods of time. Usually on the night duty or whenever I could stop long enough to just drop off for a micro sleep.

We started having accidents occur because of fatigue. Accidents with pilots who otherwise would not normally be expected to have them. One Major, who had been a test pilot, took the arresting gear the wrong way and an aircraft had to be struck from the rolls due to the damage.

The constant going also showed up in aircraft problems and maintenance issues that may well have occurred because the ground crews were also working way beyond their limits. How they kept up, to keep us in the air, I'll never know.

On one mission at the beginning of August, we were launching four aircraft early in the morning, when the runway was cool. We didn't need to worry about blowing our tires with the heavy ordnance loads we carried. We equipped the aircraft with JATO bottles for jet assisted take-off.

Taking the runway two at a time, we made a normal run until fifty knots, then punched the JATO button. It made our scooters look like rockets. The added power would get us enough airspeed to get airborne and out of the way for the next planes to take off. Then we would jettison the bottles and carry on with our mission. This time we were providing direct air support in North Vietnam.

I was to be the second of four aircraft. We were taking off in sections and joining when airborne. I watched as the first A-4 rolled and lit his bottles normally. He was well airborne before I rolled. I got to fifty knots and hit the JATO switch and the plane veered left as only the right JATO bottle fired. Shit.

I was heading for our hangar area and not the end of the runway, holding full right rudder to keep the plane on the runway for any length of time. Pushing hard, I had full right rudder and the plane was almost off in the sand when the right bottle went out and the left bottle fired. The nose veered back center such that I was now facing the field behind the tower. I was accelerating at the same time. My take-off speed was reached as I was veering right, so I eased back on the stick and took off just as the second JATO bottle quit with me in a thirty degree angle of bank, fifteen degrees off the runway heading and just above the ground.

I leveled the wings, pulled up the landing gear and turned to runway heading finally able to accelerate and climb safely out over the sea. I jettisoned both bottles. Not exactly a picture perfect take-off.

Turns out, I wasn't the only one with JATO issues. I joined up on the lead aircraft and we orbited, waiting for the third and fourth. They both got airborne normally, but one had only one JATO bottle fire and the other had to return and land when he was unable to jettison his bottles.

Whether it was lack of use, the ground crew, or the JATO bottles, is not possible to know, but when operations are going at a normal pace, everything can be checked and double checked to make sure that it works. It can't be done when there's no time between missions. And their certainly wasn't time to do so when we were flying up to sixty missions a day. It was better to just stay with standard operations and not use things we had not checked and verified prior to that time.

Sometimes I would take time to look at some of the eighteen-year-old and nineteen-year-old Marines who loaded our aircraft with fuel and ordnance. As they pre-flighted them in their tattered, greasy t-shirts and utility pants, with their haggard and worn faces they looked forty years old.

Chapter 18

∞ End of Summer, 1968 ∞

I was down to little more than three months left to go in the squadron. I had flown 140 missions by the middle of August. Had I not been out of the country for twenty days, I would have probably flown another thirty or forty more.

I was getting tired. The injuries I received the year before were starting to flare back up. Fatigue was taking a toll on my body. At some point you get so tired that even when you try to sleep, you can't. It was just easier to catnap all the time. The Assistant Ops officer caught me one day.

"Lathrop. Don't let the war keep you awake," he barked knocking my boots off the desk.

I quickly stood to attention. "Sorry, sir. Flying back end to the wall."

"Not anymore. You're doing a TDY to Japan. Need to ferry two scooters over to Japan for overhaul. Looks like you need a break."

Like a long distance was a break. "Yes, sir. No problem, sir."

Forty-five minutes later I was scheduled to fly one of two A-4s to Atsugi, Japan with Major Korman, from Seattle. He was a career Marine who had been in the squadron since I arrived. I liked him, but more than that, I trusted his flying skills.

My wife was upset that I just missed R and R with her in Hawaii, as she got ill after the baby was born and couldn't meet me. This trip would help take the place of what I had missed. Time off.

I was used to packing my B-4 bag on short notice. They gave me my 200 dollars, which was the standard allotment for TDY pay when going out of country. That made one very watchful of spending and time while away. Others had taken advantage of the trips for overhaul to stay away from the war as long as possible. Limiting funds curtailed most of that. As usual in the military, all were penalized for the actions of a tiny few.

Checking the flight schedule, I was due to fly out the next day. But my eyes took a second look at something rather stunning. I was scheduled to be number four of a forty plane flight that would join another forty plane flight and would be number forty-four in the gaggle, going to North Vietnam for an Alpha strike first – before Japan.

Looking for some liquid relief, I went to the O club, our only source of activity. Slinging back a couple of beers, I contemplated what it was going to be like flying in the middle of an eighty plane flight, forty coming from Chu Lai and forty from Da Nang. Some would be A-4s, but most F-4s and A-6s. I hoped it would not be an IFR. We had not had many instrument missions, except at night.

It was 0400 when we sat down to brief in the dark. The sky was spitting out a light drizzle. It was too early to tell if the base was under instrument conditions or not. We didn't have weather forecasts like we had in the U.S. It was often the report of the returning pilots that determined whether we knew exactly what flight conditions were in the small 160 x 70 mile radius in which we flew.

I manned my aircraft in the rainy pre-dawn. The cockpit was dry, but I was wet. My moustache and fingertips kept zapping with tiny shocks as I was going through the switches for my pre-flight. Dawn was just breaking when I checked in and found I was going to be number four on an instrument take-off, flying wing to Major Bob Korman, my travel companion for our TDY to Japan the next day.

As we taxied out, I could see that the base was overcast and the scud not above 600 or 700 feet. We would have to take-off and join on top, making a TACAN rendezvous on top of the clouds. TACAN was the main navigation instrument in tactical fighter bomber aircraft and gives bearing and distance to a station. Although we had briefed on how we would do it, in case it was necessary, we all knew it was going to be a beehive with forty aircraft TACANing at the same time in the same space. We were taking off with a normal interval. If we took off at a one minute interval, the A-4 aircraft, which carried much less fuel than the others, were taking to the air first and would run out of fuel before the mission got to the target area.

Korman and I taxied behind two Phantoms from MAG 13, who took off with a thirty second interval, or less and disappeared into the scud. Bob was in the take-off position before the second aircraft had gotten airborne and I followed, running up my engine as soon as I was in position.

"Whiskey Lima two three three. I'm on the roll."

"Roger that, double three," I responded, giving him twenty seconds before I followed. I noticed two A-6 Intruders that were already in position behind me.

My landing gear was in the well and I was turning as I ascended into the clouds at 400 feet. It was a very low overcast to be flying into for recovery, even with a radar controlled approach.

The world outside my cockpit windows was white as the inside of a milk bottle, but dark for the time of day due to the overcast. Flying north, I was climbing to 8,000 feet. I heard no one call on top and thought I should have. There was no telling what to expect. The target information and rendezvous points were not given to any wingmen, I had no idea where we were rendezvousing the two flights or where we were going or at what altitude.

Flying at reduced throttle at some 300 knots, the following radio transmissions came over the departure frequency.

"Vice Squad, this is Lovebug five zero one out of Chu Lai, over."

"Go ahead, Lovebug five zero one."

"Roger. Vice Squad, this is five zero one at 32,000 feet and we have no tops in sight."

"All aircraft in the Chu Lai vicinity, be advised that the Chu Lai radar is down. This is Chu Lai tower on guard."

"All aircraft airborne in the Chu Lai and Da Nang areas, this is Vice Squad on Guard, hold within forty nautical miles of your base."

One flight of eight had just become eighty flights of one. It was a good thing that the radar controller did not have a radar scan for the next hour. The appearance would have been a swarm of bees orbiting around the hive, all blind, all carrying loads of explosives and all coming back to the same hole at the same time. Holy smokes.

I didn't hear a sound on the radio for a full fifteen minutes as I flew five miles off the coast, maintaining my position by TACAN radials and distances. I stayed low so that I would stay away from the Phantoms and A-4s who would be orbiting higher with their more powerful engines and greater fuel load.

After the longest time, an F-4 came up. "Chu Lai departure, this is Lovebug fiver three one. Request clearance to the ordnance dump area, over."

"This is Chu Lai departure, five three one, be advised the ordnance dump area is closed due to friendly vessels in the area."

Oh my God, I thought to myself. Could this get any worse? A beehive of explosives in the air.

After perhaps another fifteen minutes, and the longest pause, while all eighty aircraft found some place they felt safe, all 40,000 pounds of bombs were dropped randomly into the South China Sea.

I figured about where I was, set my ordnance to drop and unarmed; salvoing the entire load into the ocean. Approximately fifteen miles northeast of Chu Lai, I hoped I didn't hit anything. My Scooter had plenty of fuel compared to the other types of aircraft. In addition, I was one of the first planes airborne and decided to be one of the first ones back.

Having had enough of the beehive, I decided to come in from the East. The A-6s could shoot their approach on radar, but us Scooters were on our own. I concocted an approach and arced into the base. When I got down to 4,000 pounds of fuel, well over what I felt I would need, I called out in the blind that I was coming down the 100 degree radial, starting at fifteen miles. Opening my speed brakes, I slowed to 220 knots. Putting them back in, I started a gentle guide to visual conditions or 500 feet, which ever came first. The overcast was thick and I had to watch my instruments constantly as I was descending into unknown conditions.

At 2,000 feet, the soup was just as dense as before. I eased my descent to 500 feet per minute and slowly onto the five mile arc when I broke out at less than 700 feet over a wild gray ocean, whipping up with whitecaps. I stayed on the five mile arc, unable to see land until I was only a mile away from the beach near the Americal Division Headquarter, northeast of the runway. I then moved into a three mile arc from the base TACAN and approached runway heading and turned to my final landing heading, still not seeing the runway over the intervening trees.

Now down to 300 feet under a lowering scud, I had the field in sight when I looked up and saw the wheels of an A-6, just dropping out of the cloud cover over me. Shit.

I turned immediately, right over the tree and went into a 360 degree turn while the A-6 landed. When I got back on runway heading, I saw that a Phantom was in the first arresting gear and I decided to take the second. The A-6 had disappeared, apparently making another approach. I flew low over the Phantom and took the second arresting gear, the midfield MOREST. While in the MOREST, a third aircraft, another Phantom, took the one beyond me.

Thankfully, I was able to clear the runway before the big run on it started. I was the first plane back at our line. By now, planes were landing one after another, all coming in out of the soup with no ground control to separate them. It says something of the experience of the pilots at the time. A crisis situation was handled with no more difficulty than a change in a combat mission.

Pilots in war were so conditioned to make decisions rapidly and successfully that each made a decision on how to recover and did so without negative outcomes. The constant challenges of daily flying gave them confidence to stick to their gut decisions without significant consequences. It was good to be back at Chu Lai. Semper Fi.

Chapter 19

E motionally, I was so ready for a break with this trip to Japan. Sleep came easy that night. Meeting Major Korman at the ready room, we picked up the yellow maintenance sheets for the two planes going to Atsugi. A few beers, some sun and a couple of days rest from the grind were welcome, despite the 110 degree temps.

The flight from Chu Lai to Cubi Point in the Philippines would be relaxing over what I hoped would be a clear blue ocean where I could enjoy the view. From there, we were to fly to Okinawa and then on to Atsugi. My plane had been stripped of some good parts. Therefore I had no working TACAN and was forced to rely on Bob to navigate the first leg to the Philippines.

I couldn't stop thinking about the steak dinner that awaited me at the Cubi Point Officers' Club, one of the nicer Navy Clubs in the Orient. My mouth was already watering. It was a splendid, clear day at Chu Lai.

Bob prepared the flight plan and got the weather, which showed no problems en route. There wasn't much credence in those reports however, because Chu Lai didn't get all the weather summaries.

We took off on a compass bearing to the Philippine Naval Base. Cubi Point was an air station that was also part of Subic Bay Naval Station.

The baby blue sky was clear and the ocean cerulean as we flew in loose formation toward our destination. I was comfortable and calm, flying fifty feet back in cruise formation. This relaxed positioning allowed one to keep in the pattern easily by flying the plane loosely and away from the need for constant corrections from the throttle to remain in formation.

We had an extra fuel tank in case we needed additional gas. It gave the aircraft more stability and somewhat more range. We passed the two small, sandy islands that were between Chu Lai and Cubi Point and were on course. As we did so, we started entering high stratus clouds. I pulled closer into formation and immediately got vertigo.

It seemed to always happen to me when I flew in the clouds and in formation. As we flew further east and got closer to Manila, the clouds got more dense. I had to fly closer and closer, until I was flying in parade formation, the closest of all, and the one having the greatest control by the flight leader.

We were about thirty minutes west of Manila, according to the clock on my canopy rail when I heard Bob call Manila Approach. They rarely answered.

"Manila approach, this is Hellborne two three one, inbound from Chu #$%0@."

"What?" I thought out loud hearing only static.

He passed me the lead, his finger on his earphones in his flight helmet, the hand signal for radio failure.

"Son of a bitch," I muttered off radio. "I have no TACAN navigation and don't know where in the hell we are."

I knew we were soon going to be at the Philippines, about ten minutes wide before reaching the Pacific Ocean.

"Manila approach. This is Hellborne two three one inbound from Chu Lai for Cubi Point, over," I radioed.

Nothing. Not surprising. How can a tower never answer? I was heading somewhere at 450 knots and had to do something, so I called 231-2.

"Dash two, if you can read me, click your mike."

"Bzzt Bzzt." He could hear me.

"If I am on course, click your mike once for yes and two for no."

"Bzzt Bzzt." Shit.

"If I need to turn right, click your mike once for yes and two for no."

"Bzzt. Bzzt." Holy shit.

"For every five degrees I need to turn left, click your mike once."

"Bzzt. Bzzt. Bzzt." Mother of God.

We were way off course for as close as we were, so I had 231-2 switch to Cubi approach and called.

"Cubi approach, I have two A-4s inbound for a radar pickup and a GCA, over."

"Hellborne two three one, this is Navy Cubi Approach, be advised we are now shut down and are in typhoon condition one. You may shoot the TACAN approach to a radar pickup. The approach end is zero over zero, but it is clear on the south runway. When you visually sight Cubi, circle and land to the south."

I passed the lead to the lead aircraft. "Dash-two. Take the lead and shoot the TACAN and GCA. I'll monitor radio calls. Over."

"Roger that, over."

He signaled that he had the lead and we started down. We were flying through what appeared to be a waterspout. I could just see his wing when we broke out in the clear over the numbers on the runway.

We had been advised to go to the other end of the runway where it was clear and to circle and land. I followed the no radio plane while he flew a circling approach, the normal approach made in visual conditions.

He took the midfield arresting gear and left me nowhere to land.

"Dash two, there is no one out here to pull me out. Say your intentions." His radio was obviously now unstuck.

"Roger, dash one. I'm gonna have to divert to Clark Air Force Base." I turned toward the direction shown on the approach plate to the divert field. Pulling my nose up, I climbed out of the mountains and found a hole at 10,000 feet that showed the ground below as being cultivated. I began an orbit.

When I found the frequency for Clark Approach, I found that now my mike was stuck. What the hell? I started beating it on the throttle handle trying to get the radio back. No avail. I started stacking my maps and other gear that I had in the cockpit to one side. I was getting low on fuel and had nowhere to land. Plus no radio or TACAN. I switched the IFF to emergency and tried one more time to get the mike unstuck.

Suddenly I heard, "Aircraft on the one zero zero radial of Clark Air Force Base. Turn right one eight zero for identification."

When I did so, I heard, "Radar contact, descend and maintain fifteen hundred feet. You are seven miles on the zero nine two radial of Clark."

"Roger, that," I answered acknowledging the approach to a final landing. On rolling out, I checked my brakes and found I had only one. A left brake with little braking power in it.

"Clark Approach, this is Hellborne two three one. I have very little brake. Is there an arresting gear down? Copy?"

No answer.

I repeated this call three times. No answer.

Landing the aircraft in this precarious state, I shut down the engine and slowly drifted left, finally running off the runway right where the arresting gear was hooked. Good grief. The plane sank into the mud and settled into a left wing down position as the 14,000 pound aircraft came to an inglorious stop.

As I climbed out of the cockpit, dropped to the ground and set the pins that locked the wheels, I noticed an Air Force General dressed in khaki uniform watching me. Filthy dirty in my flight suit, my day old shave and with my .45 hanging in a holster on my flight vest, I was a mess.

I knew he shouldn't be leaning on the aircraft at this point. He was just ahead of the cannon. But it was too late to tell him. I pulled my B-4 bag from the forward hell hole where the hydraulic lines are located and carried it over to his sedan.

As he walked back, he looked at his filthy black shirt and told me, "Guess you did what you had to." I held back laughter and neither of us spoke another word.

Chapter 20

B ob met me the next day, but it took five more days to fix the brakes. I slept or read most of the time during the day. We went out one night to Angeles City, the civilian town next to Clark AFB that had its usual complement of strip joints and bars for the entertainment of the troops.

We hired the standard means of transportation to get us around, a jeepney, which was a WWII jeep fitted with a top, decorated and painted up to look nice. We rode with several others headed to a club on the edge of town, but found it deserted. So we caught another jeepney. It turned off the main street and headed into the dark, unlit part of town.

"We're headed to an apartment. A gal we know."

It was a seedy cluster of ramshackle hooches. It was obvious where they were taking us, and there was some question if we would be returning.

"Hey, look. We're not into that kinda stuff. We'll just get out here," I pleaded. "Just pull over. Y'all go have fun."

"Stop here, okay?" Bob repeated. We both tried to get them to stop, but they wouldn't.

When the jeepney slowed down, I signaled Bob and we jumped out past the two Filipinos who were seated behind us. Running, we dashed and flagged another jeepney headed the other direction. Once inside, the driver started yelling.

"You in with the bad guys. Very bad. You lucky."

A big altercation followed with threats being made by the first drivers shaking their fists at us. We finally gave them five dollars, which was highway robbery, and left for the lighted areas.

We were not in as much trouble as Bob thought because I had heard about Angeles City. Carrying my pistol concealed, we could have ended up commandeering the vehicle if it had been necessary. Assuming of course that they were not armed more than I was.

We had the jeepney take us back to the Police Constabulary, just outside of the base. Bob went in and started complaining to the person who must have been the officer in charge. He was really raising hell with the officer, who in the U.S. would be a National Guard officer in the paramilitary organization.

I didn't think he was going to get anywhere so I walked over to a guard who must have been something like a duty non-commissioned officer in charge of the watch. I pulled out some twenty dollar bills. He looked interested. I gave him twenty and he seemed more interested. I gave him twenty more and he put them in his desk. Then he walked over to the officer in charge and said something to him. He now looked interested too, said something to two PC soldiers, and they disappeared for a long twenty minutes. Then they came back with the driver of the jeepney. We had been able to point him out when we came back in the other vehicle.

The Constabulary confiscated his vehicle and locked it in the yard after catching it downtown. They took him into a room next to the guard room and the sounds were unmistakable. When they came out, they had a full confession. Whether the price of justice was forty dollars for this offense, or whether I just had spent one-fifth of the money I had received for no good reason, I will never know. The results and justice were swift, either way.

We finally got away from Clark and were cleared to Okinawa, but at 39,000 feet, well higher than we were capable of flying with two aircraft with two tanks, and not fully capable of maximum thrust. They were sending B-52s and their KC-135 tankers down at the lower altitudes for Vietnam. We were not going to get clearance at any lower altitude, nor were we going to be flying at 39,000 feet, but we took off anyway, straight into the edge of another typhoon that was in the Pacific Ocean.

We climbed to 36,000 feet and there we stopped climbing, even though we were at full power. My cabin again iced up and I scratched a small hole in the ice to fly formation on the lead. I could see the ocean below and we were below a high overcast, the same as we had the first part of the first leg of our journey.

We finally reached 39,000 feet about the time we had to begin the descent into the big Air Force Base on Okinawa from which they flew the B-52s and their tankers. En route though, we heard an A-6 from Chu Lai calling in the blind that he was landing at Naha, the Navy Base. We diverted into the same base, flying a GCA and landing in a light rain, but under relatively clear conditions. I felt I had survived another combat mission. These two flights from Chu Lai and from Clark were worse than flying in Vietnam, and these trips were supposed to be a chance to get away from the war and the stress of flying in combat, not designed to test you more.

We spent three days at Naha. We would just get one plane fixed and something would go wrong with another. No one could completely fix the A-6, so it had to return with our two A-4s. We taxied out three times to take-off and taxied back with one complaint or another.

We could not fly unless all three damaged aircraft went up. We had one radio, mine, that worked regularly and only one TACAN, Bob's, that worked at all. The A-6 would be flown by Captain Suter and his Bombardier Gray Kramer, interestingly another trained forester from Maine. They had a navigation computer, but only one frequency working which was one from Chu Lai which we used in the Air Group for ground communications.

On the third day out, we just about got airborne with all three aircraft, when Major Korman blew a hydraulic line and taxied back. The A-6 pilot and I decided to go to Japan, equipment or not. He set his navigation computer, and I set my radio and IFF. When we took off, I followed him.

I found out immediately that the A-6 and the A-4 had different climb rates, and we had to stair step altitudes for him to keep from losing me in the clouds. When we finally got to cruise altitude, my cabin again iced up, making communication difficult. They had to give me a hand signal when they wanted to make a report because I was on the en route frequency and they were not.

I had no faith whatsoever in the computer in the A-4. I would trust the wet compass and the sun before I would trust it, but the A-6 didn't deviate and when we broke out in Japan, we were at 8,000 feet on runway heading after 1,100 miles. I led the approach, since I had the radio and landed first, only to have my nose gear collapse. Just as I stopped in the midfield MOREST.

It took me so long to get to Japan that I had little money or time left for me to enjoy it. I got some good meals in Japanese restaurants and spent some time sightseeing before having to catch a plane back to Chu Lai.

I caught a plane out of Atsugi and flew to Iwakuni, where I thought I would be stationed in March. To get back to Chu Lai, I then caught another flight through Taipei, Hong Kong and back to Da Nang.

Bob was now behind me somewhere, and when I got back, it seemed like I had been gone a long time. I had been on the edge of battle fatigue off and on since June. When I left for

Japan, it disappeared and came back only for short periods after that.

Upon my return to base, I there were several letters from my wife and friends of mine in the U.S. My wife wanted to know when we were going on R and R and I had replied to her that I thought Christmas would be a good time. Everyone else had gone in five or six months. Because of one thing and another, I would not be going until nearly ten months, guaranteeing me that I would get the time and place I wanted.

I read the letters and tore them up. Just like I always did.

Chapter 21

Separation from family during war is agonizing. I had a wife and a three-year-old son named Arthur when I left for Vietnam. The same day Roy Schmidt was captured, my second child, Michael was born. We had now been married for four years. As time marched on I felt further and further away from them.

I received letters from family in bunches. I posted the pictures of my wife and children, which she had sent, on the wall above my bed. Initially, I took my hometown paper, *The Dayton Chronicle* to keep up with local news. Up until that time, I had been able to keep up with a world that scarcely seemed to exist.

It didn't take long, though, before the letters seemed to be coming from a utopian society with which I could no longer identify. They were most welcome, but I had become hardened and numb to things that I had not seen in Vietnam. The letters were from what seemed to be another world. Even though they originated from where I had lived less than seven months before and were about people I knew, they now seemed to be irrelevant.

It got to be painful to think of that world because I lived day- to-day, hour-to-hour and did not think about the past or the future. To think about life in the middle class was almost like thinking about life on Mars. When viewed from my daily routine of flying, flares, tracers, bombing missions, the traumas that occurred along with combat flying and the things that went with it, home seemed shallow.

Once, I got a tape and could only play it once. It was too difficult to listen to and I could scarcely relate to the things that were said. As far as I was concerned, when I landed, I lived until I flew again. Nothing would impact me if I could help it.

Once I learned to live only for the moment, the stress of war didn't bother me. What was in the past didn't matter because it was over. What was in the future didn't matter either. Things changed rapidly. I handled the crises of the past and didn't think the future would be any worse. If it was, it wasn't worth the time to worry now. I would deal with it then.

There were too many things in the present that had to be dealt with immediately to have time to focus on the problems of my family and the things going on there. I was not sure I would even be seeing them again, though I planned on it. People I knew were dying every few days. One half of my '65 flight class was already injured, dead, or MIA. There was no guarantee the same thing would not happen to me.

We did not seem to be gaining on the NVA. They could strike at will. This constant conflict with them was keeping us flying so much, there was simply no time to think about home.

I thought the only person who felt this way was me, but the CO tore up his letters into tiny pieces just as soon as he read them, just as I did. I wonder to this day if other Vietnam military did the same thing.

I wrote home frequently, but don't remember what I wrote about because I certainly wasn't writing about what I was doing. I also kept a diary. There was no emotion whatsoever in it, regardless of what happened. What we had for dinner was written in the same tone as what I saw after a rocket attack hit our NCO area directly.

We were able to call home in the stilted language of the MARS system, a radio that called a ham operator in the states, who called your wife or family for you. You could speak to them for three minutes, but couldn't talk about anything because of the restrictions. During that time, there were hammers from the United States who blocked these conversations which were going to infantrymen, usually, in from the bush. Some were talking to their families, perhaps for the very last time.

If I ever run into one of the people who did this, I would make no attempt to control my anger. How dare they prevent seventeen and eighteen-year-old Marines and soldiers, living under conditions they would never imagine to exist, from speaking to loved ones.

Chapter 22

∞ September, 1968 ∞

W e were still flying two missions or more a day and would have each flown sixty or more missions a month, but other pilots from MAG and other units in the field took some. Collateral duties and standing the duty took time away from flying. We had flying with us from group headquarters one Marine who was approaching 500 missions, Lt. Colonel Johnson.

I was picked by the squadron to go to Base Operations every third day to stand the air base duty from 1800 hours until 0600 hours each third night. In addition, I would still be scheduled on the regular flight schedule of the squadron.

I went over and took my first night, the 2nd day of September, and had a lot of time to analyze the operations of the Chu Lai Air Station which I would be in charge of during air operations from early evening until early morning.

I got involved right away. A CH-46 helicopter from the Marine Base at Marble Mountain disappeared off the coast of Chu Lai just as I took the duty. It disappeared while over the South China Sea on instruments and was not seen again.

I was the subject of an immediate investigation as the Marines were always looking for some failure that could have caused the accident. I had done nothing wrong and they had to look elsewhere.

Several times each night, I had to check all of the runways to make sure the lights were working, there were no other problems and flight operations could continue. It was pleasant to get a jeep and drive around in the early evening and the early morning, but somewhat less so when I had to do checks at midnight or two in the morning.

Survival in treacherous conditions depends a lot on the habitual patterns you develop that keep you away from danger. Or if you react properly when put in a dangerous situation. One such occurrence happened during my night duty when I was not prepared for it.

I was surveying the base facilities with my jeep. It was dusk and the sun had set. I had just checked the tower and GCA shack to make sure they were fully manned and in working condition. I was waiting at midfield for two A-4C Skyhawks from VMA-223 to take-off. I could see them running up in the shadowy evening haze some 5000 feet down the runway. The first plane, on my side of the runway, started rolling and I could see it accelerating toward me.

I watched it approach the midfield marker, raise its nose, pull up its landing gear and start accelerating. Then it settled back on its bombs, continued off the end of the runway and exploded.

Instinctively and foolishly, I decided to be a big hero and try to get to the plane and rescue the pilot if it was possible. I could see that despite the explosion, the plane was intact.

I just started to release the clutch when the second plane went by, lifted its nose and retracted its gear, missing me by fifteen or twenty feet. I drove across the runway to the beginning of our flight line and then turned down the taxiway toward the burning aircraft. I reached its position in the sand off the south runway less than five minutes after it had run off the end. The plane was now resting on its bombs and racks.

I was not the first one to the aircraft, as two enlisted marines had come from the perimeter and were trying to get near the plane without success.

"Holy shit. The fucking ordnance is on fire. Still in the racks," the E2 screamed. The fires were burning under the aircraft in the bombs which had been knocked from the plane. "It's hotter 'n Hades. I can't get to him."

I could see the canopy was still closed and the pilot still in the cockpit. I got out of my jeep and started to go around the wing when all six 500 bombs went off, all low order. There was a big blast, literally lifting me up and setting me back down ten or fifteen feet from where I had been. But thankfully, no fragments.

"Fuckin' hell. You okay Lieutenant?"

Surprisingly, the jeep was not hurt. I was shaking like a leaf, but had no injuries that I could see. My ears were ringing and I felt like I was floating over the ground rather than standing on it.

"Yeah, I'm okay. You all alright?"

"Yeah. Damn, your jeep's still in one piece but that plane sure ain't."

"Good God, we gotta get him out," I muttered.

What wits I had still with me told me to get the pilot out, as he could be burned if he stayed in the cockpit, but when I got to the front of the plane, I found the canopy gone and no pilot to be seen.

I looked around in the dark and couldn't find any sign of him, but a shout rang out from the dark toward the coast. It was the other E2.

"Over here. I got him."

He had been blown out of the plane a good distance into the darkness by the explosion which must have lifted the entire aircraft up with its concussion. The pilot, relatively uninjured, was taken to the Americal Division Hospital.

The tower was generally good about keeping pilots in the pattern warned about conditions around the field. But sometimes they totally ignored some conditions that happened nearly every night putting pilots in some danger. It was by the grace of God that more of us didn't crash.

In '68, the Americal Division units around the perimeter were in constant contact with some enemy unit or another. Often, more often than not, this contact was on the approach to the main right runway, or the south runway. When Americal was operating, they had illumination available from mortars and larger artillery weapons. Their soldiers didn't hesitate to use it.

The tower never warned any of us, and it was not unusual to streak out of the clouds at 1,200 feet and suddenly be dazzled by two 1,000,000 candlepower flares, one on each side of the cockpit. Your night vision went in an instant. For a few seconds even the thunderstorm light in the cockpit would not give you enough illumination to see the instrument panel.

I had asked the ground maintenance crew for the base operations to pull aircraft out of the arresting gear if the base was under rocket or mortar attack. But that request was to no avail. Coming in for a landing, hearing 'Chu Lai Rockets' over the tower frequency and then hearing nothing more while sitting in the arresting gear while rockets came in around you was anything but conducive to peace of mind.

You had to keep your lights on so another plane wouldn't land on top of you and wait while the attack went on. It wasn't until after the 'all clear' sounded that the arresting gear crew would pull you clear allowing for taxi back to your flight line.

In a base of that size, near miss events never seemed to stop. There was just one situation after another that came up that had to be dealt with on the spur of the moment.

I was sleeping at two in the morning when I was awakened by an Army mechanic who had driven over from east field.

"Sir, sir," the mechanic shook me. "There's this great big white airplane sitting over by my hangar. It came in and just stopped and didn't move. I don't know what he's doing there," he said to me. His eyes were as big as two pie plates.

"What? Okay, show me where."

I had an idea what he was doing there, since it was socked-in and the runways were at minimums. When I got to the plane in the east field arresting gear, I found a pilot sitting in the cockpit of an F-8 Crusader who had come into Chu Lai with no radio. Poor guy had landed on the east field and had no idea where he was. His eyes were as big as the mechanics.

I signaled to him to shut down and he finally did so. We towed the aircraft across the crosswind runway to the main runway. I am certain he thought he landed on some matting strip in a fire base or one not manned, because he was frightened half to death.

During one night's duty I saw a tiger, or some similar animal, on the crosswind. The tiger didn't run, but kept walking just at the edge of the light of my jeep, occasionally looking over his shoulder. Tigers were reported to have been taking sentries near the DMZ and I was none too sure I wanted to find out if this one had such intentions. No one was hunting them and they seemed to be losing their fear of man. On another occasion, I ran over a black snake some four or five feet long that was probably a cobra.

Night after night was like this, but one early evening just before I took the duty, something happened that I couldn't believe. Even though I saw it myself.

I was just leaving the squadron area. The crash trucks were moving to the vicinity of the first arresting gear. But I couldn't see any aircraft coming in.

A few minutes later, still seeing nothing of the wreck in the darkness, I spotted Heislen and queried him on the situation.

"Got any idea what's going on?"

"Yes, sir. Got a Phantom comin' in that can't get its gear down."

"What?"

"Yeah, he's gonna try to take the MOREST on its drop tanks."

"You gotta be kidding me?"

"No, sir. That's what he's gonna try to do."

"Christ almighty."

"Yep, he's got that whole squadron's attention," the Corporal motioned.

I got myself in a good position to watch and waited, along with most of the rest of the Air Group in the squadron area. Then I saw the Phantom, some five miles away, approaching on a gentle glide slope. He was nose high as he approached the MOREST.

"Too high. To damned, high. Pull up. Pull the heck up," I cried out as if he could hear me. At the last moment, he did, going around again. This time, although he set up his glide closer, he was still too high.

"Holy moly. That's some bad chit," Heislen called out. "Sorry, sir. 'Bout the language."

The F-4 pilot went around the pattern again, his landing gear all in the well and no doors open. This time he was too low, but took the initiative to set the plane down and slide into the arresting gear, which flipped up over his left drop tank. It pulled the plane more than a forty-five degree angle off its runway heading and down to a speed of less than fifty knots before the wire broke. The plane skidded on its drop tanks some distance down the runway.

I was waiting for the plane to hit a light or something and blow, but the pilot hit left afterburner and turned the aircraft back toward the center of the runway. Then he hit the second afterburner and started accelerating on his drop tanks, which now were sending up a rooster tail of flames behind the accelerating Phantom.

The plane was getting closer and closer to the ground as the drop tanks kept grinding down, and the fire was behind the plane, some forty feet in the air.

When the plane got back to flying speed, he jettisoned the tanks and rotated, catching the next arresting gear and pulling it out by the roots. Arresting gear cable in his hook and with no drop tanks to land on, he eased the plane into a gentle climb, turning over the bay of the South China Sea. Both the pilot and radar intercept officer ejected, the plane making a gentle descending turn into the ocean.

I had seen some demonstrations of power of the Phantom and some other planes over the years, but never anything to duplicate seeing a plane take off on his belly with his landing gear in the well. Seeing one do so was almost beyond the imagination.

Chapter 23

∞ September, 1968 ∞

I
n addition to standing the duty, I was also flying a full
schedule. Since we were still flying up to the capacity of
our maintenance crews' ability to keep our aircraft airborne
and our pilots' ability to keep the cockpits manned, it was all
keeping us quite tired. During September, VMA-311 flew 846
sorties for a total of 946.7 flight hours.

A momentous offensive had taken place fifty miles to the
west and a large Vietnamese air base had been overrun by the
NVA. We had been flying there, as well as elsewhere. It was a
key junction and intersection point for roads into South Vietnam and access to them from the Ho Chi Minh trail.

The base was fought for by our forces, but was overrun in
just a few days, giving the NVA access into our area through
the roads to Kham Duc. The squad that got away.

I was no longer standing the base duty, and had just got off
the squadron duty. We were on the hot pad, had flown in the
morning and stood the duty in the afternoon. It was just getting
dark and we were preparing to go back to the living area and
eat. A hot pad launch came in and Major Carr and I took it,
since I had not flown since morning.

It was hazy and the sun was just setting. It was still light, but with the haze and the long distance we would have to fly, to the DMZ near Dong Ha, it would be dark before we got there.

There was no time to brief. In fact, briefs had become redundant because we followed the same procedures each time we took off. The changes could be handled when they came up. I flew so much that I had the checklists memorized and could run my fingers over the cockpit switches and set the instruments by rote.

We each got an aircraft from the line shack, lighted off and checked in on button, the squadron frequency. We called for taxi and take-off.

Rolling into the take-off position, we launched to the north and joined. As we climbed up over the haze and back into the setting sunlight we flew up toward the Dong Ha area where the sun was setting below the clouds. When we got there, we were sent to contact Fingerprint, the Marine controller that covered that area.

There was a thin overcast quite low over the target area and we were going to have to stay low. A marine squad was trapped in a shell hole by a large unit of North Vietnamese.

The controller gave us a brief. It was nearly dark and it was hard to make out the ground, much less a single crater made by a 500 pound bomb among hundreds.

There was a fire team that had been on patrol and got pinned down in a bomb crater and were now surrounded by the Vietnamese Army. We would be using our napalm and 500 pound bombs to try to get the enemy to break contact by dropping on them. Our objective was to get them to move back so the two helos could extract the team before they were destroyed. They were orbiting about three miles back waiting to get in and get the team out.

The fire team had a strobe light they were using to mark their position, but the light was interspersed with the ground fire of the enemy. The controller gave us a mark, fifty meters from the position of the team. That is so close that even during daylight hours it was like dropping on your own position.

Dash-1 called in and I watched as the ground literally burst with ground fire as he dropped his first napalm right on the mark. I rolled in as well.

"Dash two. Place your attack just ahead of the mark."

I drove right down to the ground. Time again seemed to be in slow motion. The target area seeming to be so big I couldn't miss.

I pulled off the target, pulling to the right. There was a quad fifty tracking me. I watched as four flashing barrels went off silent in the darkness. But I knew they were firing at me and following me around.

"Dash one. Turn thirty meters. Nine o'clock from the bomb crater," the controller called.

I never saw the bomb crater. Thirty meters isn't measurable at night.

But Dash-1 rolled in and laid his first two 500 pound bombs right at the controllers smoke. I followed and did the same. Again watching the quad-fifty firing as I pulled around the target pattern.

"Lead. Pull into fifteen meters," commanded the controller.

I couldn't believe he would accept, but he did, and rolled in again. Fifteen meters is dropping the ordnance on your position. It has to be sensed in the cockpit because it can't be seen on instruments. Nothing measures that close.

We were so low, we were taking heavy automatic weapon fire from the entire target area. On my last run, I had little hope of hitting the small area, but focused as much as I could and released and pulled up with Major Carr. We departed without getting a bomb damage assessment.

I had flown each run, more sensing the ground and target than actually seeing it. It was as surprising to me as to anybody how we had hit targets so close. Not to mention so many times when it seemed impossible to do so.

When we left the target area, we did not know what happened, but before we got halfway back to Da Nang, we heard that the two Ch-46 helicopters had pulled the team from the bomb crater. They had done so, according to the next day's intelligence reports with the enemy within 100 meters on every side. Our ordnance drop had made that possible.

Chapter 24

D ays ran into weeks and weeks into months. We had two or three week maintenance flights out of country and two and three week schools to break up the rapid pace of flying. The bottom line was, we did not have permanent squadrons or pilots. Enlisted maintenance men were coming and going. The squadron roster was changing every week. The new pilots were put with the experienced pilots and became experienced themselves in just a few weeks.

In September, we tried a new type of hot pad mission. Units on the ground had complained that we were not getting to them fast enough. That was probably true since we were stationed with the American Division well south of where any ground units were stationed from the Marines.

It was decided to station aircraft with normal ordnance loads at a preplanned location near the center of I Corps. When a hot pad mission was called in, the aircraft would already be airborne and could be flown rapidly to the area where they were needed. The delay would be cut to no more than ten or fifteen minutes.

This sounded good to those making the decision, but it didn't work as well as they thought. We had to guess what type of ordnance they needed and ended up with mixed ordnance loads that weren't wanted by anyone.

We took off and flew to an area fifteen miles west of Hue, just east of The A Shau Valley and took up an orbit at 10,000 feet to stay away from any other aircraft that would be transiting the area.

Since we were sometimes orbiting for three hours, I got to know the area between Hue and A Shau quite well. I could watch the air operations at Hue/Phu Bai, the Marine Air Station just below us and toward the coast. I also could see the Ranch Hand C-123s flying in flights of six or more spraying the jungle below us. They covered several hundred meters at a time with Agent Orange, killing the over-story and everything else under it.

They were definitely taking away the foliage the enemy hid under. It was the immediate need. But little did we know at the time the unknown effects of such toxic chemicals were also affecting us.

These were the most leisurely flights we flew. Because we were not going to be used immediately, we took our time and did a little sight-seeing on the way to the target holding area. We saw parts of I Corps we never flew in and saw things that we wouldn't have expected to see at all.

I flew six of these missions or more, and never one time got a decent target. We had some of the ordnance others on the ground wanted, but usually only partially of what was desired. So, we ended up carrying half or more back to Chu Lai. Landing while still loaded up.

After an hour and a half, we would have to go out to sea to refuel with a C-130. We flew to a position abeam his wing, slowing to 200 knots and moving in to take the drogue and start refueling. It was discomforting to be flying behind the big propeller. The large C-130 was in front of you and you had a face looking out the window just a few feet away.

As we were refueling, we would have to stay alert and not move ahead or out. If we got too close, the crew would guillotine the fueling hose and we would be left with it when we landed. Flying in an orbit for hour after hour was boring.

Enough so that it was not easy to stay awake. It was hard on your body too, because the plane's cockpit was so small that you couldn't move around. With long legs like mine, I would get quite cramped.

Flying just offshore was not something I liked either. We were in the middle of the airway up and down the coast. The planes that went by us were not that far away, and I was afraid one of them would hit us while we were hooked up.

Just after I left Vietnam, an incident exactly like that happened. Two Phantoms were refueling on a C-130 and were hit by two Phantoms coming down the coast. The collision sent three Phantoms into the ocean and one C-130 with its entire crew. A good idea on paper turned out to be a bad idea in practice.

Chapter 25

Completing so many missions in the cockpit of a small attack fighter bomber in less than one month, flying became second nature to me. I started feeling confident enough to make changes in the standard procedures to fit certain conditions.

Bombing and strafing took concentration and skill that required one to deviate from the normal procedures that were used because of variations in the ground, weather, enemy and friendly locations. I started developing my own techniques that worked for me, but did not expect others to use them. I learned to attack a target with guns and hit it almost every time by changing the way I approached it and the way I aimed.

Normally, when strafing an enemy position, one rolls in and keeps the plane upright while approaching the target. As the gunsight gets close, you squeeze off the rounds, pushing or trimming the plane down so that the nose doesn't rise when firing, therefore increasing speed. I never could hit anything this way. I learned a technique that worked better for me. I didn't like trimming down the nose as I was accelerating into ground fire and getting in slight negative G force situations.

At first I went ahead and made the standard upright run, but couldn't keep my bullets in the target area, which was usually shooting back.

One time I rolled in and got my nose too high so I rolled inverted. By pulling my nose down to the target I realized I could stay in positive G forces. So I kept pulling down and shooting. I put all my bullets right into the target area and when I saw they were passing over, I rolled into a ninety degree bank. Pulling back with my rudder, I then rolled level and pulled off the target.

I later improved this by rolling into a ninety degree angle of bank and strafing in the ninety degree angle of bank if I could, then rolling inverted and strafing if necessary. By rolling in with the gunsight mark over the target, I was pulling positive G forces down to the target rather than staying in a negative G situation all the way down. The only problem I experienced was if I rolled in too far away, I could not hold the inverted position and had to come back to the ninety or less degree position to get my nose higher to return and then strafe inverted.

There was a feeling of exhilaration seeing the ground and target from that position. The ground below you was speeding by so fast it was a blur. The plane's gunsight came down on the enemy and you could see the bullets impact in groups. It was this type of exciting feeling, though, that got one killed by flying into the target. It was necessary to remain totally alert for fear of something like that happening.

When flying with the Hughes gun pod, it was not possible to fly fully inverted and I stayed at ninety degree angle of bank or used the standard strafing procedure. It fired so many rounds per minute from two barrels that the plane slowed seventy-five knots and set you up in your seat, just like the speed brakes did. Flying inverted and strafing with a Hughes gun pod would get you too slow and put your aircraft in a dangerous position. So I kept inverted and semi-inverted strafing to the internal guns and rockets, and not the gun pod, though I would strafe a ninety degrees angle of bank with it.

When I first fired the gun pod and heard the growl of its 1,200 round per minute firing rate, I felt a sense of awe. Seeing the two solid red beams of tracers, each fourth one a tracer and feeling the plane immediately slow to from 450 knots to 375 knots, I felt a simultaneous exhilaration. This left me not knowing if I just enjoyed a positive experience or a negative one, but certainly realizing I had a weapon on board with a number of uses that had not yet been explored.

We had few strafing missions compared to bombing missions or missions firing rockets, usually the five-inch Zuni, which sounded like a freight train leaving the wing stations. One mission using Zuni rockets in conditions that I had previously considered impossible, showed what the A-4 was capable of, with its short turn radius and rapid roll rate.

We flew early one morning to work with a helicopter controller from the Marines. He brought us into the Hue/Phu Bai area to support some Marines down in a canyon that made contact with an enemy unit. When he gave us the mission, I had to take a second look.

He was having us attack up the bottom of a blind canyon that had a mountain at the end of it that we could not possibly get over. The canyon was deep and we would be running right up the canyon bottom to the mountain at the head of the canyon. We would then have to climb out one side or another and fly over into the next canyon and fly down it to recover our airspeed.

Once in the next canyon, we would have to descend to its mouth, climb back to altitude and enter the main target again from the bottom. I decided to try it. I rolled in low at the mouth of the canyon and the Huey popped a smoke, a white phosphorous rocket near the terminus of the stream in the bottom of the steep walled canyon.

I saw that the canyon floor was climbing at maybe ten degrees, so I just put my gunsight on the smoke and went level up the canyon, approaching the target level. The walls of the canyon were closing in. It was not a normal feeling to see a mountain ahead and the racing green jungle on both sides. I kept getting deeper and deeper and approaching the smoke, with the headwall looming larger and larger as I drew near it. When I was at the point of firing my rockets, I fired two salvos and pulled straight up, then turned to climb parallel with the slope on the left side.

I was able to climb in a steep climbing turn which was slightly more steep than the slope. My nose started getting higher. I steepened my left bank until my nose was over the horizon at the top of the ridge and I saw I was going to clear it, but nose high. I rolled into a 120 degree angle of bank, continued so that I was inverted and climbed just over the ground, but with my nose high enough to clear the ridgetop.

Just as I approached the top, the jungle crown speeding by my canopy, I started pulling a positive G force and went over the top. Inverted, wings level, I pulled down into the next canyon, rolling back to the ninety degree angle of bank. Turning down the canyon toward its mouth, I recovered to the upright, paralleling the bottom of the canyon. I had flown a wingover to the inverted position on the ridgetop and back to wings level as I accelerated down and out the mouth of the next canyon.

I found flying the recovery exhilarating and challenging, in addition to pushing the A-4 to new limits of performance. I watched my wingman do the same thing. Watching it was worse than flying it.

On my second run, my mark was even farther up the canyon than the first. I wasn't confident I could make it, but I had enough clearance the first time. So what the heck, I tried a second. This time the mountain was right in front of me, but fell back more than it appeared. I did the same thing again, but this time pulled up a canyon to the eleven o'clock so that I didn't have the initial problem of having to clear the ground so soon.

On my final run, I was light. The mark was back down the canyon, so I ran for it. Faster than normal, I pulled off with heavier G force than before. I had my nose above the horizon early and rolled inverted. Paralleling the ground, I pulled down right over the fire base at the top and rolled from a seventy-eight back into a ninety degree angle of bank. Nose level, flying over the Marines on the ground at fifty feet or less, I waved. The Marines were jumping up and down waving their arms wildly in the air.

After flying such missions, there was a certain anxiety. Flying missions where you pushed beyond limits without thinking or having ever having done it before left one wondering if he wasn't pushing well beyond his limits, or the limits of the aircraft. Flying so much gave a pilot confidence. But not all the things I did had justification; other than I was pushing myself.

We flew and landed so often that I got to where I could set up the Skyhawk in trim at the 180 position and try to land hands off, using only the rudder. It wasn't that hard after a few times to come close. But even trying it when we were in battered planes that could have suffered battle damage was not a safe thing to do.

On the 24th of September, Lt. Colonel McCrary presented awards at the Change of Command Ceremony. I was being promoted to Captain and decorated as a pilot.

"For heroic achievement in aerial flight in combat action of the Republic of Vietnam, Captain R.G. Lathrop is awarded not only one, but two Distinguished Flying Crosses."

Corporal Heislen gave a shout of "Oohrah" which was simply not done. I must have turned beet red. I had flown so many, I wasn't sure for what missions I was being given these prestigious medals. I did not know until much later that one of them was for bombing and strafing a non-existent enemy battalion some six months earlier at My Lai. That memory would haunt me.

Chapter 26

At the end of September, I got temporary orders to fly with the USS New Jersey as an Air Controller in North Vietnam. I was approaching six months in the squadron and would be leaving in seven more. I had to go to school to learn the procedures for controlling a ship as they were quite different than controlling artillery and other aircraft, which I already knew how to do. The school was at some remote base on Okinawa and I would be leaving in a few days, though the orders had not yet come in.

There were almost as many pilots needed in the ground forces and as air controllers, as there were in the tactical squadrons and helicopter squadrons. Flying for seven months straight was about as long as one got on the stick. However, maintaining your minimum flight time was still required. Even while in another unit away from Chu Lai.

Flying in MAG 13, which had no A-4s except for two-seat control aircraft would allow me to keep my seat time. Those going to infantry units would have to come back every month or so and get in a few hours and then return.

MAG 12, VMA-311 at which I was now stationed, also had a couple of two-seat A-4s. They were two of the ones we had brought over in January of 1968. I was scheduled to fly on a mission controlling the USS New Jersey, a battleship that looked as big as half the fleet that was now stationed off North Vietnam just north of the DMZ. I had seen it firing quite a number of times, but had not seen the results.

I was supposed to brief with a Lt. Colonel from the Group 79 Staff. He met me at the flight line and we had a short brief before we launched. I would be flying the plane, a TA-4F, one I may have flown across the Pacific to Da Nang the preceding January. The F-100s and TA-4Fs that were flown by the Marines and Air Force in North Vietnam were two place jet aircraft. They had a higher survival rate than the small 0-1, 0-2 and OV-10 control aircraft that were used in South Vietnam. The jet aircraft were able to fly higher and had more room to install the necessary radios to be able to talk to the ground forces, the ship and other aircraft.

I heard the pilots who flew for the battleship talking about controlling it from the first time that we sent aircraft up to do so. It was not the same as controlling artillery, as I had learned to do when in Basic School infantry training. The battlewagon fired only one shot and not several at a time. To get first on line, we'd fly over and under. Firing for effect, then we'd set off all guns firing after the bracket had occurred as did artillery pieces in unison.

We manned the aircraft. I would be flying the TA-4 while the Colonel spotted and controlled the radios. He instructed me to keep in a constant climbing turn to keep the guns from being able to track us with radar because we would be changing airspeed, altitude and direction simultaneously.

There was a high overcast as I flew up the coast to Dong Ha. I could see the battleship off the coast about ten miles from the North Vietnam beach. It stood out as it was larger than any of the other ships of the task force it was attached to by at least three times.

The Colonel checked into Dong Ha and got clearance into North Vietnam. I flew across the DMZ near the coast and proceeded up fifteen or twenty miles to a target area the Colonel had worked before.

I could see roads below us converging here and there, but no targets of consequence. I was busy trying to position the plane so that the Colonel could see the area in which he was working. This required constantly changing direction and altitude.

"Lathrop. Check out that large tract of trees. See where the road converges?" he barked over the intercom. "Head there. I think it's gotta be a truck park or some kinda storage area. Reports are this pattern's been changing over the last coupla weeks."

Later, when flying along the Ho Chi Minh trail, I found that this was the way to determine enemy usage and intentions. Roads and trails would start getting wider and not growing shut. Bombed out bridges would be rebuilt and the pattern would extend to a certain area, therefore making it was possible to tell where the trails were leading.

I set up a horseshoe pattern around the suspected truck park and began my orbit behind the target while the Colonel called for a shot from one of the ships sixteen-inch naval guns.

A large gray blast 6,000 feet below us showed where the gun had been laid to fire.

"Damn. Five we're short." The Colonel made a single correction. The impact was short and 1,000 meters to the south.

"BB-62 add five hundred and go right by a one thousand." A few seconds later, the entire grid square of 1,000 meters by 1,000 meters exploded in dust, fire and flame. It was truly impressive.

A radar or visually controlled gun position opened up on us from some 500 meters south, just north of where we were flying.

"BB-62 we're taking hits. Salvo at radial zero seven zero." The gun emplacement and everything around it disappeared. I took a deep breath feeling my hands shake. The Colonel was cool as a cucumber. We had to return to the tanker to tank and called Dong Ha for clearance out of North Vietnam.

We flew south to the DMZ and across to where the tanker was to be stationed, but were unable to take fuel and had to return to Chu Lai. We flew back down the flight corridor to the base and landed. The Colonel gave me a long debrief that taught me more in fifteen minutes than I learned later in Forward Air Control School. He had been controlling the USS New Jersey since it came to South Vietnam and knew all the ins and outs of flying to maneuver it to success.

There was a clear and continual danger in flying, both in North Vietnam and spotting for the ship. The southern part of North Vietnam was covered with anti-aircraft guns. Any time they wished to open fire they could do so with effective results. Those results could be made more effective if they also fired missiles so that you had to dive down into the low thin overcast of gray, lead-lined clouds. The fact they chose not to do so, always made me wonder if we were hitting anything that was affecting their ability to pursue the war.

The second problem was the New Jersey itself. The projectiles were fired nearly straight up, rather than directly at the target. When they came down, they were quite close to the horseshoe orbit of the planes doing the spotting for them. Armed with proximity fuses, it was just as possible for their rockets to go off near the planes controlling them as near the ground and the enemy positions.

The Colonel warned me about flying the horseshoe pattern too close to the vertical points above the target and therefore becoming a target myself. During the next month, while I was in Okinawa training to control aircraft, the ship and its artillery shot down two of its controllers. One pilot ejected over the fantail of the Jersey, but the plane, instead of drifting away and crashing safely into the sea, continued to orbit and nearly hit the ship.

The USS New Jersey could fire nearly half way across the southern portion of North Vietnam. It could also fire across the coastal plains of South Vietnam where most of the combat was taking place. If we had possessed three battleships and had the ammunition to keep them firing, we could have covered nearly one-half the area all our planes flew in North Vietnam. If the ship would have been allowed to be as effective as it was during the few times I saw it fire, we would have saved hundreds of the planes we lost. But unfortunately, that was not our government's strategy during this war.

Chapter 27

∞ October 9, 1968 ∞

What a beautiful day it was. Normally, when I awoke anywhere but in Vietnam, I felt a moment of joy that I was greeting a new day. I would then look outside to see what the day was like and what I would be doing.

At Chu Lai, I would awake and feel the moment of joy; for perhaps one-half of a second. Then lying in my sandy bed in the Quonset hut, when I was lucky enough to be in one, my mood would languidly sink into a sick feeling in my stomach when I realized where I was.

October 9, 1968 dawned cool and clear, much like the climate in which I had always lived, near the mountains of SE Washington State, Northern Idaho and Montana. When I walked out for the first brief, my flight suit did not soak through with sweat as normal, but stayed dry. The weather was unusually cool and clear. I stood at the top of the sandy hill where the Quonset hut was built, looking over the South China Sea and took in the stunning morning.

It was going to be an easy day. I had one scheduled flight and then the duty, but the squadron was not going to fly in the PM because we had six hours of stand down. We were taking the hot pad at 1800 hours. At that time, I would have the squadron to myself. The only activity happening would be the day crew loading aircraft for the hot pad scheduled for the afternoon.

I briefed for a 0700 launch to the area around Camp Carroll, west of Dong Ha and perhaps seven miles inland on the highway to Khe Sanh, which was now abandoned. Lt. Barger, a new pilot, was slotted to fly with me on one of his first flights. We met in the squadron area, checked out two aircraft with bombs to be released at 2,500 feet, not at ground level and took off to the north.

The day was as clear and bright as any I had seen anywhere. The South China Sea sparkled as did the ships on the sea and in Da Nang harbor. I flew several miles farther out to sea than normal and over the large island that lay off the coast of Da Nang, something my exploring nature had wanted to see for some time.

We had been flying almost every aircraft available in support of Thuong Duc, inland between Da Nang and An Hoa. It was ten miles southwest of the big base and four northeast of An Hoa. An attempted insertion by CH-46 Marine Corps helicopters had failed. All the bombing had not stopped the ground fire from shooting at the insert, effectively preventing it. I could see the area as we passed it flying beyond Da Nang.

It was possible to see completely across South Vietnam as we flew north to the Dong Ha area. The mission seemed to be something other than the combat objective to destroy enemy bunkers as was described in the brief. It seemed to be too idyllic a day for a war.

After landing, I made a trip to the living area. I wanted to get a clean flight suit so that when I stood the duty, the air would be breathable in the ready room. With the ability to wash our flight suits in the water we caught from the air conditioner, it was no longer necessary to wear our flight suits until they stood up by themselves in the corner.

We had food available at the flight line, which was two miles or more from our living area. So I went down, took the duty, signed in the log book and got a sandwich. Opening the door to the 8x40 trailer, I prepared for a pleasant afternoon of reading, napping and doing little else.

For the moment, the base was almost silent. I wondered what had happened to the assault on Thuong Duc, because we had thrown so much at it.

During the afternoon, the cool air breezed in the open door as I read. I looked out across the flight line to the mountains to the west of Chu Lai, they seemed benign enough. But in actuality, they shielded huge enemy units the size of divisions, using the area beyond them as a rebuilding area.

The flight line was wet from the occasional showers. The flight line crew was present at times loading ordnance for the night launches if they came. At about 1720 hours, I heard my replacement coming early, Steve Argabright, a former cadet and now a pilot with 100 or more missions.

He was standing in the door, in his flight suit, talking to me, when a hot pad launch came over the field phone. The mission was to work an area we had never flown before. The Americal Division held a location just south of our base. It had been declared unsafe to fly over. We were to stay at 1,000 feet or above when making an approach to the north runway.

In the absence of any pilots in the ready room, Steve and I left the truck driver, Frenchy Ouellette, in charge of the squadron. We took two planes loaded with napalm and 250 pound bombs used against the enemy to break contact when they were attacking U.S. forces.

We took off to the north just before sunset. Despite being cloudy and broken over the land, it was clear over the ocean. A typical situation with which we had become accustomed.

We joined abeam the O'club and proceeded south to the field boundary. The target area was almost in the field flight pattern. We made landfall at the West German hospital ship that was anchored some 4,000 meters from our target. It was a neutral ship which treated all Vietnamese. We could now see the target from the coast.

As we flew on inland, both Steve and I noted that there was not a sign of conflict on the ground below. It looked like Vietnam must have looked before the war. But the intact appearance was deceitful, as it was one of the thickest areas of Viet Cong in our sector. It had not yet been assaulted with any large size units and bore no scars of such an action, as other areas to the north did.

The sun was just setting as we approached the controller, who gave us a mission to attack the only intact village I was ever to see. As I looked at it, I saw only the peaceful appearance of the Vietnamese countryside in the setting sun and no sign of any enemy.

Although the village appeared pleasing in the setting sun, nothing was known to be benign in this area. We napalmed the village and left it burning, the flames nearly one hundred feet in the air. We then went to a hill above the village while the village was additionally bombed by two Phantoms. We left as they strafed what had been a peaceful country scene in an area that was yet to be destroyed by war.

After landing, Steve took the duty and I went to the O'club. I bellied up to the bar and took a seat next to another pilot. He stuck out his hand open palmed up for a brother-type hand shake. "Pete Erenfeld. Tomcats, too." he pointed to the Tomcat patch. His skin was tanned from the sun. Brown eyes and a short Marine buzz.

"Gene Lathrop. Nice to meet you."

"I'm doing some TDY with MAG 13. Been on many runs yet?"

"Too many. Seen lots of craters up and down the coast."

"Ain't that the truth."

"But not today," I rubbed my brow.

"Oh, yeah? How's that."

"We napalmed what looked like a peaceful village. It got strafed by Phantoms afterward."

"Yep. My Lai. Flew it yesterday. Probably full of tunnels of VC. That's our job. Taking out the gooks. How ya like the scooter?" taking another chew on his cigar.

"Love it. Light. Maneuverable. Great bird."

He downed the rest of his pop. "Yep. Sure is. Time for a Kodak moment."

Donning an Army combat helmet, he had me shoot a picture of him. He was holding a huge .45 caliber grease gun automatic weapon he had obtained. A bandolier of ammo was slung across his shoulder with a lit cigar in the right corner of his mouth to complete the look. His call sign was Blackcloud. Maybe we'll fly some together."

"Maybe so."

I noticed he wasn't drinking. He was typical of so many of my wingmen. Confident. Good looking. Taking the world on one day at a time. He noticed me eyeing his glass.

"Nothing but Coca-Cola. If I'm gonna be flying, I lay off."

"Good man."

"Seen too many brothers make mistakes."

As it happened, we would become not only wingmen but friends. Erenfeld was every bit a rogue, macho jet jockey. Exactly opposite of me. But one good pilot recognizes another.

It was still cool and now clear. The stars were bright over the South China Sea. Just as the club was closing at 2200 hours, the squadron truck driver came in to the bar with the operations officer.

We had just received the biggest launch of the war off of the hot pad. They needed every pilot who was still be capable of flying to man the aircraft for the launch.

"See what I mean? Ya never know," Peter patted my shoulder.

The operations officer determined I was one capable of flying. Though I had some reservations after Peter's comments. I had flown two missions, stood the duty and now had consumed several beers.

The decision to accept the mission was made by me and no one else. I went back to the squadron area and took an aircraft up. Moving into position behind Maj. Jim Lent, we flew toward Da Nang and Thuong Duc which was in danger of being overrun.

I was so tired and had enough alcohol in me, that I could not stay in formation. So, I drifted out some 500 feet and flew to the target area, which was now covered with clouds that came up to the ridgetops on both sides of the valley. Though a higher overcast, with no moon showing, the tops of the clouds were not all that clear.

There was a hole in the clouds at the upper end of the valley. The mouth of the canyon was clear, but everything in the canyon was under the overcast which was less than 500 feet above the ground.

An air controller was beneath the overcast and flying in the vicinity of the target. He was in an OV-10 which could turn in small areas and could go slow enough so its pilot could maintain control of the other aircraft and the situation on the ground.

In order to drop our ordnance, we would have to penetrate the clouds at the upper end of the valley. Keeping instruments down until we flew out under them, then we would pick up the target, drop on it and climb up and out of the clouds back on instruments again. It was too dark below them to fly down the canyon under the overcast at our speed with any safety. The valley was narrow with side ridges that we would be in danger of impacting if we flew out the bottom to the mouth the valley.

The lead two aircraft off the hot pad were leaving just as

we arrived. Lt. Colonel Overturf, Executive Officer of the squadron and Captain Sandlin were not able to get onto the run-in line, make the approach and bomb safely. They were now out of fuel and leaving for Chu Lai. This left six of us to try to get under the overcast and attack below the clouds to hit the enemy, which were putting a Marine unit in danger of being overrun.

I couldn't see any way to get under the clouds without flying into the ground. If I had been flying a slower aircraft, it may have been possible, but not at the speeds we were flying. I had never really been in formation and was now flying behind the number four aircraft as number six. He was flying so far out of formation that he was alone as number one instead of number four. Whether this had anything to do with the fact that we were the only two to have been put into the formation out of the bar, I could not ascertain.

Suddenly there was a flare over the target area under the clouds and the plane ahead of me called in and rolled into the clouds. I saw him disappear. It was Captain Donovan who was out of formation, but just at the head of the valley. I followed his track and saw the white light of his bombs explode under the clouds. I kept my eyes on my instruments and my heading toward the area where I saw the explosions. Not accelerating to 450 knots as usual, I kept my airspeed down, flying 300 knots down through the clouds. My power back switches were armed and ready to drop.

I broke out under the cloud layer and had only an instant to make a correction. I saw the fire from the napalm burning. Making out the narrow ridge system the controller had been talking about in his briefing, I made the correction, salvoing my whole load. I pulled back into the clouds, nose high, since the steep side ridges were on both sides of me. I watched the airspeed bleed off to 125 knots, just as I broke clear of the clouds. More than twenty degrees nose high. I eased the stick forward to zero Gs and the plane went ballistic with no lift on the wings. It slowed to below 110 knots. Falling back into the clouds, nose low, in an angle of bank of less than ten degrees I accelerated to flying speed while steering for the coast, which I had seen when I popped up.

I broke out of the clouds leaving the mouth of the valley and flew back over the South China Sea landing back at the base at Chu Lai just before midnight. We waited in the ready room as each of the pilots came back singly. All without bomb damage assessments. I wrote up the controller for a decoration since it was his actions that assured the mission was completed safely. Definitely not ours.

Taking the duty six by six back to the squadron area, I went to the mess, got something to eat and took a shower. I was in bed at 0130, having been up nearly twenty-two hours. As I drifted off to sleep, I took a sigh of relief. This all could have ended very badly. I was lucky to not be dead. Erenfeld was right and I never took another drink before a mission. If it had not been for the initiative of Captain Donovan and the ability of the air controller to describe in terms we could understand what we would see, there would have been no ordnance dropped.

Chapter 28

We enjoyed some slow times due to bad weather, but with the exception of those few days, we had flown almost constantly since January, when the TET offensive began, forcing everyone to operate to their limits. Had I not gone to Japan twice, I would have flown nearly 300 missions in six months, with seven months more to go. As it was, I had more than 200 missions and still had one month in the squadron.

There were jobs in the Marines for pilots other than flying. Usually, after six months or less, a pilot could expect to be transferred out of the day-to-day stress of flying a helicopter or jet in combat. They were transferred elsewhere to fill a position either at the Wing level or with a Division in the field.

In my opinion, the most disliked of these ground positions was an assignment to a battalion in the field as a forward air controller. To me, this was the direct opposite of flying. But my wingman, Pete loved his assignment to the OV-10.

It was expected that if one did get assigned such a duty, it would last six months. If the pilot completed the six months and had a few weeks or a month left, he would return to the squadron and fly for the last few weeks in country. Pilots had to stay qualified. It was mandatory. As such, the divisions allowed each air controller with them to return each month to fly enough to keep current.

I flew with some of these pilots who had not flown for some time. Sometimes, their proficiency had deteriorated to the point that they were dangerous in certain types of missions. I experienced the same lack of prowess after periods of absence off the stick time and it took some getting used to its power again. When flying in close contact with friendly forces, we became, for short periods of time, as much a liability as an asset to those around us.

Finding yourself behind an aircraft, a stranger in the cockpit for a few minutes, was unsettling. Not having your bombing runs develop as you expected, surprised you, as much as it must have those who were flying with you. Your wingmen had come to expect you to do certain things and for short periods of time, you were no longer capable of doing them.

I had one wingman that had been gone for several months. Upon his return, he dropped his load right on the friendly forces and not the enemy. Fortunately, he missed them with his ordnance, but he had dropped on the smoke they popped to show their position rather than on the one used to mark the enemy position. He was an unusually competent pilot, but his skills had deteriorated during the time he was off the stick.

The A-4 was good at making last minute changes when on the run-in to the target. With a flip of the wrist, the gunsight could be moved fifty to one hundred meters and a correction made at the last minute if necessary. Usually, it was when the smoke was away from the true target, but you picked it up on the run in.

It was also necessary to stay alert at what was said over the frequency in the target area. The enemy monitored our frequencies. Even though they were coded, occasionally bogus calls were made in English for corrections that would not place the plane or ordnance in a place they could hit their assigned target. These spurious voices came out of Laos and had both American and foreign accents. They usually were asking for things so far from what we normally did that they were nothing but a nuisance, but one wondered who they were and what they were doing in Laos helping the NVA.

Another situation that occurred was when a friendly unit was being overrun. Interestingly enough, it was similar to the last scene in the movie *Platoon*. The general scenario of combat in South Vietnam was that prisoners were not taken. The NVA could be especially brutal when overrunning a unit and the unit's last airstrike may well be called in on themselves as a last hope of survival. When they did this, usually the pilot would not know. They would say on their last broadcast 'hit the green smoke' and then pop a green smoke grenade, leaving the aircrews overhead to wonder what had happened when all the radios went silent.

I had one advantage over the other pilots of the squadron. Over the months that I had been flying, I was also keeping up the intelligence reports. I knew what operation I was supporting and what units were in the operation. If we were away from an operation of any size, I knew we were dealing with a patrol or other small unit action. Since the controllers on these small units were not as proficient, it was necessary to take more caution in operating around them. It was best, if an airborne controller could be brought to the vicinity because he was more familiar with the ground around them and the operations they were on. It was not always possible to do so and our effectiveness was reduced accordingly.

Chapter 29

∞ October 10, 1968 ∞

H aving been up for most of the preceding day, I was lucky and not scheduled to fly until the afternoon hot pad. That would most likely be two missions, but they would usually be over more by early afternoon. I looked forward taking a dip in the ocean, having a nap and taking in whatever the evening offered.

I flew one mission early in the afternoon, but nothing came up later. I waited in the ready room in case something did come up, rather than have to be called from the living area and make the long trip back.

While waiting for the squadron six by six, a hot pad launch came in from a unit near Camp Carroll. Captain Forney, whom I had lived near back in the states in 1966, was available. We took the launch and flew in the near darkness past Da Nang to a point just south of the DMZ. It was not quite totally dark when we turned inland and were skirting the DMZ en route to our target. It was in a valley we had never flown to before, but which was near the area I had seen the 144 helicopters on fire.

Just as we made landfall, it seemed all the guns in North Vietnam opened on something, though I could not see what. It was truly a spectacle to behold as we flew some five or six miles south of what appeared to be the flashing lights of a large city. There were guns firing everywhere. From small arms to 100mm guns causing explosions in the sky as high as you wished to look. I had a hard time focusing on our mission with all that going on just north of us.

Captain Forney was another of the pilots in our squadron with whom I had gone through flight school at the Marine Training Squadron at Yuma. He was now at VMA-311. We approached the target area in the first valley inland off the coast just south of the DMZ. An OV-10 was the controller, and he gave us a mission not unlike the one of the night before.

Our target was an enemy position at the head of a blind canyon, with the main units just half way up the hillside. We would have to run up the canyon bottom, with rockets and guns, attacking the hillside which faced us. Then climb over the long low ridge to our left, coming around, and firing again.

It was hard to tell where the bottom of the canyon was, and it was hard to tell when you got to the right position to fire in the darkness because there was poor depth perception. We had enough ordnance on board to make thirty runs if we had to. I started my first run well back into the valley, lowering my nose and accelerating down the valley floor, with everything black on both sides of me and the headwall of the canyon facing me. Things I could barely sense were going by me on both sides in a blur.

As I approached the headwall, I placed my gunsight on the center of the hill. Firing all sixteen rockets, I saw them hit, telling me I was too close. This forced me to rapidly pull up and roll banking to the left, rolling over the ridge and down the other side where there was no enemy ground fire.

On the second run, it was even blacker than the first. I armed my Hughes gun pod and ran again down the valley near the bottom. Pulling up near the headwall at the head of the canyon, I pulled the trigger, sending a two-second burst into the area of the enemy units.

Two solid red tracer lines tore into the hill and I could see them bouncing around after they hit. The plane slowed to seventy-five knots and forced me into the straps of my seat harness. I was in the floor of the valley and pulled the two beams up the hill, doing a little soft shoe on the rudders, sending red beams back and forth over the lower one third of the headwall.

I was slow this time, but the ridge was not high. I pulled up easily and rolled over to the other side and climbed back to my roll-in altitude. The third run was the same as the second, but I increased my airspeed so that I had more remaining after the burst. Again, I could see the disruption the bullets were causing all over the hillside.

They were flying in every direction, every fourth one a tracer. The tracers alone looked like they totally covered the target. After the second gun run, whatever had been there was gone. We were released with less than ten percent of our bullets used. This was the first and only time I ever fired a gun pod at night. The number of rounds going out and coverage of them was astounding to see. The amount of lead going out had to be tremendous to slow the 16,000 pound plane as much as they did. I would not have liked to have been on the receiving end of the fire.

We flew back down the coast. The guns were still firing in North Vietnam when we flew back toward the sea, though I never saw exactly at what they were firing. After checking over the planes, I went into the ready room and found that I had immediate orders to Okinawa for Forward Air Control School.

I tried to beg out because not only had I already seen hundreds of air strikes controlled and flown in control of the New Jersey, I wasn't going to go with a battalion to the field.

Besides, I didn't need to learn about something I wished to avoid.

Logic was never a cause to change preconceived actions. As such I went back and again packed my B-4 bag for another trip out of country with 200 dollars to spend. Before leaving, I went in and checked on the intelligence reports I would have to turn over.

A red-haired male was seen leading an enemy patrol near Da Nang. Another group of Caucasians, probably deserters, were operating near Hue independent of any unit. There was a report on the total number of deserters and from where they had deserted. I skimmed what were the last reports I was to see and wish now that I had been transferred one day earlier. The number of American deserters almost made me ill.

Chapter 30

I flew on a C-130 to Forward Air Controller School at Camp Butler on Okinawa. The fifteen pilots, all junior officers, could have taught the school rather than been there as students. We had experienced more aircraft controlled in the hundreds of missions we had flown, by more types of aircraft than ninety-nine percent of the military pilots that had ever worn a uniform in all the countries that had air forces. The school was redundant except for the special training on the battleship and on some new procedures that had been developed. We could have figured those out on our own had it been necessary.

On the last day, we had a chance to use all the radios. In my experience, usually the weakest link in any military maneuver had been the radios. I found that to be true, as we were never able to control any of the planes that we were flying due to the radio breakdown.

The school was finished in five days. We had two days to get back to Da Nang. As previous experience had shown, we were told that we would be in big trouble if we didn't get on the C-54 that was flying there the next morning. Commanders warned they would make special examples of us if we stayed in Okinawa any longer.

That was double jeopardy, as far as I was concerned. As pilots they had already committed the worst assault to us that they could by taking us out of the cockpit and sending us out as forward air controllers in other aircraft, or with the infantry battalions. If they really wanted to punish us, they had done so already, so the next morning the plane left nearly empty for Da Nang.

One week later there was a party at the Naha Officers' Club. Having little money left and nothing else to do, I went to the party and found most of the FAC school there, broke and planning on returning the next morning to Da Nang. As luck would have it, we had to stay three more days before a plane could be found to take us back for the reward of our efforts.

I had three days left in the squadron when I returned. I flew my last mission with VMA-311 and landed, looking forward to my new job in Marine Air Group 13 as a forward air controller flying the TA-4F in North Vietnam and Laos.

Captain Argabright and I, who had flown the mission south of the base where we had attacked the intact village and left it totally obliterated, were met on this last evening by Major Stanley McGeehan, the Assistant Operations Officer of the squadron. We completed the checks on the two planes required each month. The inspections were done to make sure everything was correctly connected and placed on the aircraft. He handed us a write-up for a Distinguished Flying Cross from the Americal Division General Staff for the mission south of the base.

We both declined to authenticate it, as Marines had a dual authentication process. The medal had obviously been written up for some other mission and mistakenly sent to us. If it was not a mistake, then the Army had a loose definition of the reason such a medal was to be awarded. We agreed we did not wish to be decorated for a mission that didn't deserve such recognition. Especially a mission that was one of the easier ones we had ever flown.

Chapter 31

∞ Marine Air Group 13 Chu Lai, RVN ∞

By the time I was to be transferred to spot for the battleship and work as an out of country air controller, I knew I wasn't being sent to a job that was sought after by anyone. That is anyone besides, Peter Erenfeld. He loved his time as a controller. Flying a horseshoe pattern for hours on end in North Vietnam was risky at best. As previously noted, the ship had now lost two or three controllers of the eight that were controlling it from the Marine Corps.

I had already flown once in the aircraft spotting for the nine sixteen-inch guns and was developing in my mind how I could improve on what the Colonel, who I had flown with, warned against. I racked my brain, but had come up with nothing. Suddenly, the problem was solved. President Johnson called a bombing halt in North Vietnam and the battleship was to move south.

The day I heard this, the 28th of October, the plane I was to be flying, and the crew flying it disappeared in North Vietnam. Once more, I was going to replace a casualty. He was an American Indian pilot, a Major, who had gone through Yuma with me and tragically was lost on his last mission before rotating back to the United States.

The next morning when I caught a ride over to the new air group, I thought my orders might be canceled and I would be sent somewhere else. Neither of the two A-4s that the squadron used as controller aircraft were available to fly. One had just disappeared. The other was in Japan for overhaul. There were already two A-4 pilots in the group, both of whom had just arrived there. Thus, more would be unnecessary. None of us was qualified to fly the F-4B Phantom that the squadrons in MAG 13 flew and therefore would have to return to MAG 12 to get our mandatory flight time.

I was surprised that they signed me into the group. I was sent to maintenance to work with the new computer maintenance system. They chose not to send me elsewhere.

No sooner had I checked into maintenance, I was transferred temporarily to Operations to do the MIA investigation on my predecessor. Probably due to my Intel experience. I was going to learn a lot about his past few weeks. The task was to try to make a determination on what happened to him and the Navy doctor who was observing in the back seat. Clearly, a violation of the Geneva Convention rules. As if there were any actual rules during war.

Since I had been told this report was a priority and superseded everything else I was to do, I got all of the information about the disappearance and took a C-123 to Dong Ha, where the radio and radar controller to the flight was located. I was able to interview the controller who was talking to the aircraft just before it disappeared.

They had both visual and radio control of the aircraft just before it ceased transmitting replies to their radio calls. But the aircraft was not the only one with which they had contact. There were several who heard rumors or saw things that may or may not have been happening in the vicinity of the TA-4 as it left North Vietnam. Their contradictory statements were not only confusing, but didn't shed any light on the disappearance.

This disappearance was one of only two I had ever known to occur in broad daylight.

I finally declared the plane and its crew MIA and yet still did not have any idea what happened to it. With thousands of choppers, ships, and troops located everywhere for miles in every direction from where the plane was last seen, nearly to Hue off the coast, I thought it impossible that such an incident could occur. But it had and two more aircrew were listed as MIA. They remain so to this day.

The disappearance of the last TA-4 left Captain Cook, who had been in the same units I was in since 1964 and Captain Butt, who had flown with Major Connor for a month before I checked in, with no aircraft to fly. No one was going to check us out in the Phantom, so we had to find our own place to get flight time.

Captain Cook went back to fly with VMA-211. I went back and flew for several weeks with VMA-311. I felt uncomfortable flying so rarely. I felt my skills were deteriorating. Not wanting to drop on any friendly forces, I tried to find another place to get flight time. It was fortunate that such an opportunity occurred at just that time.

Each Air Group had one C-117, a Navy version of the C-47 flown in WWII. It had bigger engines, a longer fuselage, and retractable gear. It flew fifty knots faster, significant when you are talking about 125 knots cruising speed, but was propeller driven. The C-117 was a transport. None of us was qualified in it, any more than we were qualified to fly the Phantom.

The Hummer, as we called the C-117, was flown on non-combat missions during the day ferrying troops from one base to another. It also flew combat missions at night. When airborne for five hours at a time, the Hummer served as a flare ship over troops on the ground, carrying forty flares and a crew of thirteen. Both uses were common and the planes were flown a lot of hours.

Although I had zero hours in the C-117, there was a constant need for co-pilots. It was determined that all of the A-4 pilots would be allowed to fly it, both on the day and night missions. Since we would have a qualified pilot in the left seat, we could be taught the intricacies of flying propeller driven aircraft by the pilots who flew them, all of whom had more than a thousand hours in type.

I had actually flown propeller driven aircraft in the distant past, but not of this size and certainly not multi-engine aircraft. I took the test and learned enough to start the plane without backfiring the starboard engine. Thus, I was scheduled for a warmup test and landing qualification shortly thereafter.

The commanding officer of the squadron, responsible for air group maintenance, was Major House. He was one of two Black commanding officers in the group and took me on my familiarization flight. He was a patient, calm pilot who allowed me to make my own mistakes and correct them myself, rather than take the plane and make me start again.

I got the engines started and taxied to the take-off position on the south runway. The big fuselage and the tailwheel were things I was not used to and the taxi down the taxiway was slow, deliberate and wandering.

I taxied into the take-off position and ran up the engines. I checked everything, the props, the mags, all of it. Releasing the brakes we started rolling. I was used to taking off in a jet. I got the plane airborne, the gear up and trimmed for flight and looked out. I wasn't three fourths of the way down the runway and everything was done. The plane was trimmed for flight with the gear up and nothing to do until I landed.

We flew for an hour or two, more than an A-4 could stay airborne and then returned so I could practice landing. There is one thing a jet aircraft will do better than any other aircraft. It will come down.

Much of its lift comes from the engine and when its power is pulled back, the jet will drop like a rock. Not so the fat wing C-117. When I got ready to land and pulled the power back, the plane floated in the air. It drifted slowly down on the runway passing below me as I overshot the first time. I landed near midfield, bouncing half a dozen times before finally setting it down on the wheels.

Over a period of an hour, I learned to take-off, land and fly on one engine. That was enough to qualify me for co-pilot. I found that after qualifying, I was scheduled the following day for the passenger run to Da Nang. I would fly both the morning and afternoon run. I was flying with an all enlisted crew. The pilot was a Sergeant, one from WWII and would be the plane's commander. I would be his co-pilot.

I loved to fly. So flying any new airplane was a challenge for which I couldn't wait. The next day, the 11th of November, the day after the Marine Corps birthday, I was going to have my first flight on the flight deck of the C-117.

Chapter 32

E arly on the 11th of November, 1968, I went down to my office in the hangar that the group air base squadron used as theirs. We were responsible for the rest of the flight line and the integral parts of the F-4 maintenance. We had been assigned only three aircraft, one of which no longer existed and the other which was still in Japan for overhaul.

I met the enlisted crew at the C-117. Starting the engines, I checked them out and taxied to air freight to pick up our load of passengers for Da Nang. It was cool and damp, possibly eighty degrees, with a hundred percent humidity.

I taxied up to the air freight building in the C-117 looking out the side window, feeling like I was taxiing a B-17 for take-off to Germany from England with the 8th Air Force. The plane I was flying was built in 1944, two years after I had been born.

The air freight NCO gave the flight mechanic the manifest. There were two soldiers carrying M-16s and flack vests who looked to be thirty years old. They took back seats and threw their rifles and packs on the deck and lay down to catch some sleep.

The remainder of the passenger manifest was comprised of several floor show personnel that had entertained Marines the night before. The Marine Corps Birthday celebration was celebrated regardless of where we were when it was time to do so.

The young women were dressed as though they were flying from New York to Boston; rather than from Chu Lai and its sand to Da Nang and its red dust. They sat in the center seats and along the litters that lined the fuselage next to the rows of windows.

The Sergeant pilot glanced at me and shook his head. Reading his sign, I started the starboard engine, which backfired but didn't blow a stack and he the port. He again nodded. The wind seemed too strong for take-off from the main concrete runway

"Tower this is Charlie Foxtrot one zero two. Ready for take-off."

"Charlie Foxtrot zero two be advised winds are two seven zero at twenty-five."

"Roger. Request taxi back to Air Freight." I said thinking we would abort until the wind died down.

But the Sergeant, whose glasses were so thick I wondered if he could see over the nose and to the pitot tube, had other ideas. "Tower, CF one zero two. Is the crosswind available?"

"Affirmative, CF one zero two."

We were directed to taxi to the crosswind runway, which could not be seen from the mat we were on. It was reached by taxiing down the perimeter near the overrun of the concrete runway on a narrow taxiway that could not be seen from the passenger compartment. At 4,000 feet long, it lay between two rows of barbed wire that marked the perimeter of the matting strip. It was perpendicular to the main runway, but a quarter of a mile from it.

Because the wings were low and moved up and down as we taxied down the taxiway to the crosswind runway, we had wing walkers on the wings picking them up, or stepping down on the concertina on each side of the taxiway. There were sounds coming from the cabin that sounded somewhat like chickens in a coop that had been invaded by a fox.

I reached the crosswind. Had I not been the base duty officer, I would not have even known where it was or how long it was. Having had to check it a number of times, I knew how long it was. At only 4,000 feet, it was about 2,000 feet shorter than I would have liked it to be.

The pilot just sat there waiting until I ran up the engines and checked the mags and props. Not knowing what to do after that, I pushed the throttles forward and waited to see what would happen.

We veered, first one way and then another, as I used differential throttle movements to keep the plane in the center of the runway. Halfway to the take-off point, the main gear ran over the catapult and the plane bounced and returned to the runway. I was approaching the end of the runway. I never had to do anything before when I got to the take-off point because everything had just happened, but that didn't appear to be the case now.

With 500 feet to go, I pulled back on the yoke and shouted 'gear up.' We flew through the clearing between the trees that had been cleared at the end of the crosswind, and out over the South China sea, less than twenty feet above the water, with sounds coming from the rear cabin compartment now bordering on the shrieking level.

Climbing to 1,000 feet I set the props. It was pretty along the coast and the ocean below was blue and peaceful. I flew to within ten miles of Da Nang when we were forced to climb into a squall and shoot an approach over the harbor. I was operating the radios and the top Master Sergeant was flying the approach. The squall was pouring rain into our cockpit from the escape hatch over the center console where the throttles and mixture controls were located.

The first mechanic gave me a poncho to put over the controls. The rainwater fell on the poncho and drained back into the passenger cabin and presumably went out the back door. I couldn't see it from the co-pilots seat. It was now totally silent in back.

We broke out nearly 1,500 feet above Da Nang harbor and the Sergeant pilot gave me the controls with the plane flying with full flaps in an attitude I had never seen any plane in before. We were wings level more or less, but dropping straight down.

As I approached the runway, I flared. Boy did I flare. The next time I touched down, I had six thousand feet of runway left. I pulled up the flaps and taxied into air freight.

I have often wondered, if we had been in an airliner taxing into the passenger terminal in the U.S., would that flight and landing have had any effect on the next passenger load. Because the young women flying in our plane had jumped to the ground hugging each other, with tears in their eyes. They ran from the aircraft like it was some monster trying to devour them.

The two soldiers aboard were still asleep, it hadn't bothered them at all. We had to wake them up to catch their next flight. Reloading, we returned to Chu Lai without any problems. I was now fully qualified in the C-117.

I went on to fly fifty combat hours in the C-117, including flare drops from Da Nang to the DMZ. It was a forgiving aircraft and not nearly as tiring to fly as the jet aircraft I had previously flown. It had a large cockpit where it was possible to get up and move around. Also, it flew slow enough so your mind was not racing all the time from one thing to another to keep ahead of the aircraft. Plus, it was not deafening inside the cockpit, a factor when flying jets that left you exhausted in and of itself.

The flare ship missions were all four to six hour night missions, unless the ground unit requesting the illumination wanted more than one flare at a time. They were not scheduled, but launched off the standby flight schedule. When we flew the flare ship, we flew with nine in the flare crew and four or five in the cockpit. The plane would be loaded before sunset and the crews would be on the standby flight schedule. If we were called for illumination, we would man the aircraft, usually between 2200 hours and midnight.

We would climb to 2,500 feet or above and fly to the area the illumination was needed and slow to ninety knots. The pilot would fly the plane and the co-pilot would man the three radios. One to the ground control of the aircraft, one to the flare crew, and one to the ground forces. I would put one earphone on the right ear, one on the left and one behind my left ear to try to keep the mikes straight as I ran the flare drop.

We carried forty flares. If we dropped on each run, we dropped for 160 minutes, or more than three hours over the unit. There were times when the ground unit below us was under attack and we could see the tracers, as well as hear some of the radio calls of the action below. It appeared unreal from the altitudes we were orbiting and it was only possible to catch part of what was going on. It left a sick feeling in my stomach to be so impotent while the combat action was going on. It was not unusual to take-off at 2200 and not land until dawn, or just before. We would sleep for two or three hours and go back to work or flying.

It was a different type of flying. There was time to think before you had to take any action and not just react according to a preplanned course of action like in a tactical aircraft. It was not nearly as tiring as described before which made it not nearly as difficult to make the decisions that had to be made.

It was hard, however, to let another pilot take command in difficult situations and to tell you what to do when no one had ever done so before.

There were six or more Majors and Lt. Colonels who flew the multi-engine aircraft. They were all plane commanders. The shortage was in qualified co-pilots. There were three of us qualified minimally to fly the plane as co-pilot. I enjoyed the change, but given the opportunity, would have stayed with my first squadron.

Captains Cook, Butt and myself were anomalies in the air group. None of us flew the main type of aircraft they flew, none of us had flown with crews, and we remained somewhat the "butt" of jokes. The Phantom pilots considered themselves above those of us who flew the scooter, which was much smaller, more maneuverable, but only carried 3,000 pounds of bombs. It was somewhat archaic in the inventory of aircraft, already being declared obsolete and replaced by the U.S. Navy. Our reply? At least we could hit the target.

Chapter 33

∞ December, 1968 ∞

I had to go to Da Nang on some routine maintenance business. It was always time consuming to do so if the C-117 from our air group or MAG 12 was not flying because we had to depend on whatever showed up at our air freight and make do with it.

I went over to the Air Freight building at 0630, hoping to get to Da Nang and back the same day. I was near the top of the manifest. I had a book with me and lay down on the concrete floor to read while others came and signed up for the air traffic that came through to take them where they were going.

I read and slept all morning, but no plane came that was going to Da Nang. It was nearly noon, so I took my name off of the manifest and went over to our mess hall and got something to eat.

I had just missed a C-123. It was taxiing out of air freight onto the runway, running up its engines as I left the mess hall. Walking back toward the air freight building, I put my name on the next manifest.

The C-123 was rolling as I walked across the road. It lifted at midfield and climbed for two or three seconds. Then the engines started missing. The plane slowed, but kept flying for a few more seconds, then dropped a wing and disappeared. It returned to view when it rolled wing-over-wing and settled in a cloud of dust. Smoke rose from the area, near the end of the runway. Having the feeling I did about burning to death, I sensed what was going on in the plane.

I didn't have anything in the way of emotions left about things like that and put it in the back of my mind to deal with later. A C-7 of the US Army stopped at air freight and I got a ride to Da Nang in it.

We finally got back the TA-4F that had been sent to Japan for overhaul. It was a nearly new plane with everything in it functional and working. We brought it into maintenance for a last check before taking it on a test flight.

Captain Cook and myself took the plane out over the gulf of the South China Sea that was just off the base. We climbed to 20,000 feet and checked all the controls. The plane flew superbly and would trim up straight and level. Something the older planes we got from the Navy would not. They would fly within varying attitudes depending on their past record of landing and overstress conditions.

The TA-4 was perfect, but we only got two-thirds of the way through the test hop, when the fuel transfer light came on and we had to land with the emergency fuel selected. After landing, we found the plane had been fueled in some way so as the main tanks were full of sand.

Fueling problems just don't occur. It is the easiest kind of problem to prevent, but two planes had now had fuel contamination of the worst type. Not to mention it happened to two different kinds of aircraft, fueled by two different Marine fueling crews.

Since I was in maintenance and quality control, I tried to pin down the cause and could not in either aircraft. There was nothing in common between the two, but for some unexplained reason, we now had one aircraft lost and another whose future was in question. Turns out both had bizarre fueling problems. I didn't have to deal with it for another week.

* * * * *

I missed going on R and R to Hawaii twice and now was going to be able to go. I had gone so long without leaving that I was at the top of the list for the air group. Even though I was so close to ending my tour, I wasn't going to give up this stress relieving opportunity.

I dug around in my sea bag and found the dress uniform that I had taken into country for going on R and R. I had not checked the sea bag for some time and had to throw away most of the things in there because they had mildewed. The uniform was okay and I had it pressed, found some ribbons at the Americal PX and got everything ready to go.

I went to bed in a heavy rainstorm two nights before I was to leave, with everything ready and prepared to catch a flight to Da Nang and then to Hawaii the next evening and following morning.

At 0600 I was awakened by the sound of incoming. It was hitting close, as there was the sound of explosions, not just the sound of the rockets going over, a sound like a freight train passing.

I rolled out onto the concrete floor until the rockets subsided. It was time to get up, so I walked halfway to the shower room when a second rocket attack was launched toward our living area, the impacts less than fifty yards away.

I was in the middle of an open area and ran to the cover of a sandbagged Quonset hut, but felt a burning on my foot as I got behind the building. I looked down and saw the ground covered with blood.

The wound was caused by a hot piece of shrapnel or a piece of the metal pallets the rocket had hit. Either I stepped on it or it hit me before I could get totally in the protection of the sandbagged building.

It was not a serious wound. The skin had been taken off the bottom of one third of my foot, but other than a burning pain, it was something to be overlooked. Unfortunately, it would not be overlooked when I got on the plane for R and R, my first priority.

I went to the corpsman and had the wound cleaned and bandaged. "Say, can you clean this up for me?"

"From the incoming?" the corpsman asked.

"Yep."

"Sure you don't wanna go over to America?"

"Hell no. I'm scheduled for R and R today and unless I'm bleeding from some artery, I'm going."

"Gotcha, man. I gotcha."

The corpsman cleaned the wound and bandaged it up. In this climate, any wound could be deadly if not taken care of. Everything abscessed or got infected if it was left open, so I had the wound well cleaned, then bandaged, so that I could get my dress shoe over it. After I did so and the foot swelled, I couldn't get the shoe off, but I could walk far enough without a limp to get on and off the plane and not appear to be injured.

The big wigs didn't want soldiers, sailors, or marines hobbling down the gangway off the aircraft after they landed at Honolulu airport. I caught the evening flight to Da Nang on one of our C-117s and the following evening boarded a Boeing 707 for Hawaii. I wondered what it would be like to see my wife again. It seemed like I was leaving one world for another. It gave me horrible anxiety.

Chapter 34

∞ Christmas, 1968 ∞

I had put in for R and R in Hawaii twice. Because of illness, I had been unable to go. My wife had been pestering me via letters on exactly when it might take place. I decided I would put in for the seven day pass to Hawaii on Christmas, as it would be nice to be with my wife during the Christmas Holidays.

There were perhaps 200 soldiers, sailors and Marines that met to go on the Boing 707 at Da Nang. We flew to Anderson Air Force Base on Guam and had a two hour layover, then flew on to Hawaii. It was good to be clean and on our way to somewhere other than someplace in Vietnam feeling relaxed and rested.

I felt like an old man with the enlisted men on the plane. I had a wife and two children and was twenty-six years old, one-third older than most of them. We flew all night across the Pacific. Halfway to Hawaii, we watched the recovery of a manned space capsule by the US Navy. It reentered the atmosphere and was picked up by an aircraft carrier that was over the horizon from where we were flying.

We landed at Honolulu and found out there were few rooms for us because the civilians had rented most of them for the

Christmas holidays, leaving few for the daily R and R flights from Vietnam.

This had been made known to the population of Oahu, apparently over radio. Private homes were made available to those of us who did not have accommodations and everyone was quartered during the week.

My wife did not meet me at the airport, as it was not known for sure when I would arrive. I took a taxi, with a soldier and his wife, to the private home where they were going to stay. Then I went out to Black Point where my wife had a cousin with whom we were going to stay. I had been up nearly two days.

Seeing her for the first time was awkward.

"Hey, there." She ran to me and throwing her arms around my neck. "I'm so glad you made it. Finally."

Although she was hugging me tight, I stiffened. It was more like meeting someone for a first date, than seeing my wife of four years.

"What's wrong?" she asked, pulling back from me.

"Nothing. Nothing at all," I shrugged trying to save face.

"I'm so happy to see you. Tell me all about what you've been doing."

I had no idea how to answer that. Did she really want to hear about the villages with children I had napalmed? Did she want to know about the deserters and fragging? Or maybe about the pilots I had seen shot out of the air.

"Oh. Just flying in a war. That's about all."

She reached into her pocketbook. "Here. I brought you pictures of the baby."

I looked down at the photographs of the son that had been born while I was away. He was now about four months old. "He's pretty cute," I managed choking back tears.

My heart was breaking as I thought about the time I missed seeing my son as a newborn. I didn't know him.

"You can keep one. I brought you a small one, so that you can take it back with you."

"Thanks. I will," I flatly stated. The lump in my throat was thick. I tucked the photo into the pocket of my jacket.

Luckily, the lush scenery was so exquisite; the sight of it distracted her. At this point, I had been gone so long and had changed so much, that it took some time to get reacquainted with her chirpy, happy conversation. It seemed so foreign to me.

Later, in the privacy of her relative's home, I prepared to take a shower. A real shower. What bliss. My wife let out a gasp when she saw the wound on my leg.

"Good heavens. What in God's name is wrong with your leg? You're wounded." She clearly had not been prepared for that visual. She turned pale and her hands were up over her mouth in horror.

"It's nothing. Just some superficial shrapnel."

"But Gene. Are you okay? Do you need to see a doctor?"

"Nope. Just need a shower and to re-bandage it."

"You need medical attention," her face was still contorted in concern.

"Not no, but hell no. Do you want our R and R to be over?" I was adamant.

"But how can you even get around?" she worried.

"It's nothing. Now let's get going. We need to enjoy what time we have." My wife looked surprised at the intensity of my reaction. I was normally a pretty soft spoken guy. But lots of things had changed about me. A hell of a lot of things. I wondered if she really knew me, her husband, at all.

Her cousin had booked an endless array of activities and the week passed quickly. We were graciously taken to see all the sights on the island. I requested to eat out at restaurants away from the main crowds, finding that I was jumpy around a bunch of civilians.

It was during nighttime that I found myself to be the most uncomfortable. One would think that being away from your spouse for so long, the first thing you would want to do was jump her bones. After all, I was one of the pilots over there that had remained faithful. But I found myself uncomfortable to even be in bed next to her in negligees. I was so used to sleeping in a sandy cot by myself.

I knew it hurt her feelings. On a couple of nights, she reached out to hold me during the night. But I could only turn away. By the third night, I realized that I had to make love to her. I knew she wanted to. Almost mechanically, I got into bed next to her and began to kiss her. Reaching down, I fondled her breasts gently. I noticed that she had remained slim, even after having our son. I ran my hands down over her hips that I no longer recognized.

I heard her moan in delight as I quickly rolled on top and entered her. But after a few strokes, it was over.

"I'm sorry. That I came so quickly," I apologized.

"No. No. It was fine," she explained. But I knew it wasn't. I knew my wife questioned what had happened to me.

Except for the trip to the Punchbowl, a military cemetery in a volcano crater in the center of Honolulu, the sights were pleasant. On the day we visited, a military cortege was present. They were burying casualties from Vietnam that must have occurred just as I had deployed. It was more than I could take.

We celebrated Christmas dinner with my wife's family. Afterward, we went to a party given by local Honolulu families. My wife looked pretty in her turquoise, sparkly party dress. Although she chatted and seemed to be having a good time, I still found it hard to make small talk. I had just completely lost track of current events.

On the last night, we went to a floor show at one of the big hotels on Waikiki Beach. Many of the persons on my flight were there. We were all in uniform since we would leave the hotel, go straight back to the airport and Vietnam. Most looked too young to be in the military at all. Their wives looked like children to me.

At the intermission, the entertainer, Tommy Sands, asked all those in uniform to stand and tell their unit. I listened to them. Most were from combat units in I Corps. Looking at my fellow passengers, I felt sad because I knew that many of those soldiers enjoying the night's festivities and lifestyle were going to be seeing it for the last time.

"Penny for your thoughts?" my wife asked as we said our goodbyes.

"You wouldn't want to know," I said remorsefully.

"Robert Lathrop. Maybe you underestimate me?" her lip quivered.

"I'm sorry." Again, I put on a mask and pasted on a smile. I didn't want to disappoint her. "I had a great time. It was wonderful to see you again."

"Be safe, Marine." My wife blew me a kiss.

"Will do," I shouted back walking out to the tarmac. I couldn't make myself turn around to see her standing there in tears, waving. I just didn't know her. Or anything anymore.

It wasn't easy for me to return to 'Nam. Having now been back stateside and seeing how I just couldn't relate, the thought made my stomach turn over. Where did I belong? I just didn't know anymore.

At 0100, I boarded the aircraft, went to sleep and woke up sixteen hours later as we approached the anarchic landing pattern of the massive Da Nang Air Station. Getting off the plane, I changed out of my dress uniform which had wilted in the heat, put on my flight suit and went back to the war. Sand. Dust. Toxic humidity. Afterburners. So much for R and R.

Chapter 35

No sooner had I returned, I found out a friend of me and my wife's, who was also a pilot and had gone through flight school with me, had been shot down over Laos some two days before.

Through Intel, I researched the situation. Captain Kent had been on a night mission. The pilots both appeared to have vertigo in the target area, west of Khe Sanh and in Laos near Tchepone.

There was no organized search by Red Crown because the area was so heavily manned by NVA guns. Unfortunately, the possibility of getting a pilot out was determined to be nearly impossible.

On occasion, there were crewmen found by individual flights in areas where they had been thought to have disappeared permanently, but later shown up when another aircraft or helicopter spotted them. Although it was unlikely here, I worked that sector before. Maybe I might have a chance to spot the chutes, hear radio calls, or see the impact point of the aircraft as was known within a few miles.

I got as much information as possible and set up a grid search on a map of the area, hoping that I would see the impact point of the plane.

I was unable to get a co-pilot to go along to the Khe Sanh area. But I set up a grid and searched for nearly an hour. The jungle was so thick and high that no hole could have been seen. I did see enemy movement within a mile and the movement of the troops in the area was right through the middle of where the plane had been shot down. Only a few enemy were seen, but their actions indicated no critical situation was occurring in the area. I had no luck whatsoever in finding the location.

When I got low on fuel, I flew down the Ho Chi Minh trail. The F-4B of Captain Kent had been shot down within a few miles of the A-4E Roy Schmidt had flown. That was only a few miles from the F-10 of Aerial Cross. Both of those pilots had been in my flight class of May 9, 1966 in Meridian, Mississippi.

The Ho Chi Minh trail was obviously heavily used, but during daylight, there were no vehicles in sight. The next month proceeded as the previous one had. We made daily attempts to fly the TA-4F, but could not resolve the fuel problems. It was not always possible to get someone as a pilot so that I could spot and not fly.

I started taking the flight line personnel who were responsible for the airplane. When put in the back seat, they would fly erratically enough so that no enemy guns could track us in North Vietnam where we were now flying to keep track of the North Vietnamese activity there during the bombing halt.

The battle ship had moved south and was positioned off the coast of Chu Lai. It was shooting over the base and into the mountains beyond, west of the base. This was harassing fire, but it was harassing me, too. The shells sounded like a dozen freight trains flying over the air station and continued for twenty-four hours at a time. Additionally, B-52s would arch around the same area. They dropped an amazing number of 500 pound bombs in a single line. It would create a sensation like an earthquake; throwing you around in your bed or hut, or making the ground jump, if you were outside.

The naval gunfire going over, the artillery going out, rockets coming in and Phantoms taking off in afterburner all sounded nearly the same. I never quite got them differentiated enough to keep from rolling onto the floor each time the sounds occurred, keeping me constantly awake during the times the shooting and incoming was occurring.

$$* \quad * \quad * \quad * \quad *$$

Mishaps were inevitable with all the flying going on. But sometimes they were just tragic. While I was on R and R, one such instance occurred.

I found out that on the 18th of December, fourteen soldiers burned to death in a C-123. It had been fueled incorrectly by the transient ground crew. Jet propellant had been put into the tanks instead of the aviation gasoline used with props. Another mishap which thankfully, I had avoided.

With all the problems going on, I was transferred to Da Nang to learn how to use the complex computer sheets and maintenance records I was now getting. My interest in these records was waning because I could not understand them and was losing the desire to learn. It rained the entire time I was at Da Nang, so hard, few planes flew.

We finished the maintenance course and three of us were put first on the manifest to go back to Chu Lai. The rain continued, so no planes left. However, planes did come in leaving off troops to go elsewhere.

For three days we sat, gathering even more personnel at the MAG 11 living area, many of whom were key officers in units elsewhere. Finally, it was decided to bring a CH-46A to the wing pad and take as many of us south as could be carried.

It was pouring rain when the helo landed at the wing pad. The chopper looked like it had been in the war since the first day. It had all the windows out and was beat up from the cockpit to the ramp. The pilot, a Major, looked like he hadn't slept in a week. There were two .50 caliber machine guns in the front windows with two gunners there.

The crew chief loaded about twenty-five persons on the chopper and said they would try to get airborne. The Ch-46 was started and the pilot engaged the rotors and tried to lift out of ground effect. The chopper started to shudder and shake. He set it back down, kicked off five persons and tried again. I would have gladly been one of them. The Ch-46A had been modified, but their reputation of falling in two pieces out of the sky did not give me any confidence regardless of how much they had been modified.

We got to ten or fifteen feet and the pilot lowered the nose. We began accelerating along the perimeter of the west side of Da Nang, gaining no altitude, but gaining airspeed. When we approached the river south of Da Nang, we turned down it at less than a dozen feet and began accelerating so we could get over the bridge. After doing so, we stayed right on the water until we went out over the ocean, then stayed at 500 feet, in the rain showers, as we flew down the coast.

Helicopters don't fly straight. The rain came through the side windows like BBs hitting the skin and clothes. It wasn't possible to avoid them.

Apparently, Chu Lai was under instrument conditions because we climbed into the clouds, getting beaten and soaked while we flew an instrument approach to the south runway.

I was fully fed up. Even when I flew the C-117, the occupants were dry, even if uncomfortable with my flying. I was both miserable and disenchanted.

We finally broke out, never having needed to go into the clouds in the first place. Everyone was relaxing when I noticed we were going into a hover. I wondered what was going on until I looked out the open window and saw a Phantom below us, on fire, with the crew in the cockpit and loaded with 750 pound bombs.

I got up out of my seat and screamed as loud as I could to get the hell out of there before we all went up in the same explosion. The crew would never get out with us holding the canopy down with the down blast from the rotors.

There was no way he could hear, but either mental telepathy or his realization of what could happen caused him to start flying down the taxiway to our flight line. Just as we got there, the Phantom blew, less than a mile behind us. The crew had escaped.

I walked over to VMA-311, as a new transient line was constructed near their flight line. I found that the TA-4 we had been flying had been put on a ship and sent to Japan. We tried to clean the fuel tanks unsuccessfully a number of times. We still had not located the problem with fueling the plane.

We now had no planes to fly as reconnaissance aircraft, but three pilots attached to the air group to fly them. I wanted to return to VMA-311 and fly with the squadron, as did Captain Cook. Captain Butt had too little time remaining to be transferred and would be remaining at MAG 13.

We were given a going away party and orders to Da Nang, with less than three months to go in country. While we were at the party, with our bags packed, I was joking with Captain Cook when I noticed, as I had noticed for some time, he was not the same as before. He seemed unlike his previous self. I had known him for four years, had flown with him, been in squadrons with him, and completed OCS with him.

It was then I found out that he made the same change I recognized in others. He had been shot down over the South China Sea while I was on one of my trips away and had changed. He now had the same look I had seen in other pilots who experienced the reality of a crisis, rather than just seeing it happen to others.

Without any desire to do so, Captain Cook and myself boarded a plane for Da Nang the next day, the 10th of February, 1969. Change was the name of the game in the Marines.

Chapter 36

I had flown out of Da Nang enough times that I knew I didn't wish to be stationed there. It was spread over an area of several square miles. With the harbor, transient facility, and large complement of Navy, Air Force and Marines was too big and too complex for my liking.

It became much less to my liking when I checked in and they checked my records. They found I had been initially trained in Basic School and knew something of infantry tactics and leadership. Therefore I was sent to be the company commander of the infantry company that defended the west perimeter of the base and was responsible for internal security as well.

I was dumbfounded. I had gone to Basic School by a mistake of orders. I recalled that according to Lieutenant Weatherford, my recruiting officer, the Marine Corps did not make mistakes. I graduated in the bottom ten percent of the class. I never had a platoon and now, here I was taking over an experienced rifle company where there were no other officers but me. I was just at the point of checking into the company when I saw that I was scheduled to fly.

I didn't see how I could fly and have a company at the same time. I suddenly had 150 Marines to take care of and had not even checked into the unit.

I went and briefed for the flight. Missions came first. We were going to North Vietnam, down the Ho Chi Minh trail and then from Khan Duc to Da Nang. The route I flew a number of times before in the TA-4 that had been barged out with the tanks full of sand.

We took off to the north. I was in the back seat and we were climbing through the dense haze over Hue when the engine started cycling up and down in rpm. We were unable to control it and pulled back the power, turning back toward Da Nang. I was starting to feel jinxed. I had not been in an airplane for three months except the C-117 that had not had some notable fuel problem.

We flew back to Da Nang. When we landed, the engine was still cycling up and down by five percent or more. We taxied into the chocks and the plane wouldn't shut down. It started to slowly auto-accelerate and got to eighty percent when the flight crew chocked it and chained it down. At eighty percent, the brakes would hold for a while, but not if the plane accelerated more.

It was hard to get out of the rear seat with the engine running, but I did so and returned to my company headquarters. I found out that I would have three platoons, would have five Marines on two shifts responsible for internal security and that there was going to be a major offensive in less than a week.

I had to start somewhere, so I had my predecessor, who would be leaving shortly, introduce me at the first night formation where we assigned units to positions and organized for the defense. I had fifty new Marines from the air wing, but the remainder were highly experienced, some with three purple hearts and others having extended so they did not have to return to the garrison duty of the U.S. They would be discharged in the U.S. at Treasure Island, near San Francisco when their enlistments were up.

I watched my predecessor handle the evening guard formation and decided to take command right there. He had no training or experience, was a First Lt. bombardier navigator in an A-6 and had no business being assigned as he was.

I had the three duty sergeants, my platoon commanders and all their Marines return to clean their weapons and get an adequate supply of ammunition. I instructed the experienced to tell the inexperienced the basic facts of how to use a weapon at night. We did not have the most modern weapons. We had M-14s, a fine enough weapon, but different than the field units who had the M-16.

After making sure each had a weapon he knew how to use and was with someone experienced, I sent them to their night defensive positions and brought in the three platoon commanders and the night security commander.

All were buck sergeants. Three of them were black and all had good records. In interviewing one, I relieved him on the spot. He had personal problems, as I found other black Marines to have that I could not comprehend, much less resolve. I transferred him to a less demanding job and then left the area, leaving the remaining sergeants in charge.

We had intelligence reports of a large-scale offensive in just a day or two. An enemy battalion had passed just a few hundred meters from our perimeter the night before without being challenged or seen.

The Lt. who was my predecessor, was sent back to headquarters. After we inventoried the Armory, he was sent to Wing for disciplinary action. We had many weapons unaccounted for.

After I was transferred to Da Nang , I started taking possession of weapons, vehicles and equipment that were left at air freight by those going on emergency leave that did not come back; or those that were delivered or left with no one to pick them up.

I now took stock of our weapons, vehicles and other unaccountable items. We were accumulating things so fast that I could not decide what to do with them. Much of the equipment was coming from other units who passed through Da Nang and who left it there, or it came from aircraft who left it for units that were not stationed close enough to get the equipment to them. Weapons of all kinds were left and so were M-60 machine guns. Since I had an armory and a bomb dump, I was given some of this material to store.

At the time, we didn't have enough vehicles, machine guns and other weapons. I decided that we would use those things that we were storing. I had no idea where most of it came from and I doubted if those units that lost it knew where it was. So, I put it to use. With a bomb dump, armory and flight line to use as a storage area, I accumulated enough weapons and vehicles to equip a small unit. All unaccounted for somewhere.

Rather than store it, I finally put this equipment to good use. I had an almost impossible time getting equipment and replacements from the Marines. Often I could be heard berating their constant inability to supply me.

"Sergeant," I bellowed.

"Get me those requisitions we sent last week."

"Right away, sir."

Thumbing through them, I knew straight off the numbers didn't match.

"Damn it. Not again. Sweaters. It's ninety degrees and they send me sweaters."

"No socks, sir?"

"Hell no. No socks."

"Sorry, sir. Sure could use some. Mine's been mended so many times my toes have permanent air conditioning."

Maybe they knew what was available and didn't bother to send what I asked for because they knew the system better than I did.

Knowing that there was an abundance in vehicles, equipment and artillery, their inability to supply me would be overcome by the relative abundance elsewhere. Their expectations were that I would find it on my own, eventually. Black market or not. Why couldn't we get something so basic? Socks. Perhaps I had found the Marine Corps Supply System and put it to use as they had planned; by keeping me constantly without what I needed.

Chapter 37

I learned quickly about my unit. It was so experienced they needed little more than direction and support. The Sergeants, who were platoon commanders, only had to be told once and the work got done. I had to keep on top of the current situation and handle the personal problems, which numbered in the dozens and things ran smoothly. Rank meant little to them. They, by and large, worked together for their mutual needs and their mutual needs included keeping the base secure.

They were violent in combating those things they felt threatened them. In the barracks, they would not tolerate either thieves or homosexuals. When these individuals were found, usually, someone would notify me. I would have them taken into protective custody for their own safety. If the statements were true about them, I had the homosexuals transferred to Treasure Island for discharge and the thieves written up and dealt with under the local command.

By and large, the Marines I had caused no problems. The problems that occurred that I had to handle were from individuals passing through the area, or were race-related problems that were hard to identify and harder to resolve.

There were not only black and white uniformed servicemen at odds, there were more situations where blacks were at odds with each other. Since they were from other units, I did not identify the sources of the problem, but there were times when I thought we were close to a race war without even knowing who would be in it. My platoon commanders, all of whom could have been made officers, complained that they were being called Uncle Toms by other blacks because they were trying to use the Marines as a way to get ahead.

I told them they were achieving what they set out to do, and they shouldn't let others stop them from achieving success. We had excellent intelligence about the units that were going to be attacking our base during the 1969 TET offensive.

* * * * *

I had been flying for some months over the trail they were using to bring the NVA regulars into the Da Nang area. When the attack became imminent, I moved to a Quonset hut next to my command bunker and the reports were exact as to when and where the MVA would attack. I checked out a .45 grease gun for my own use and had my radio jeep ready the night we were supposed to be hit. I only had to wait until 0100 and then the incoming started coming in.

The first battery of rockets to strike hit the flight line and killed three Marines and started a fire in the fueling tanks along the flight line. Within ten minutes, the deep water pier bomb dump was hit. A shock wave went over the base. I could hear a .50 caliber machine gun firing to the south and see helicopters. The crackle of firearms could be heard to the west, but far enough away to be no immediate problem.

After an initial barrage and then a few isolated rockets and mortars, the attack seemed to stop. I took the jeep and checked the perimeter and found no problems, but also found we were no longer alone in defending it. The Marine First Tank Battalion had moved in front of the bomb dump and living area.

While I was there checking our unit, the tanks got an order to fire. I could see some type of action well to the west. The tanks fired in that direction, the main avenue of approach to Da Nang and whatever was there didn't pursue what they started. I went to bed at three, but woke up with another rocket attack at dawn.

This time, they got a direct hit on our bomb dump and on the large fuel tanks near the flight line that must have held 500,000 gallons of jet fuel. Rockets of 2.75mm were flying everywhere. Billowing smoke, black and oily, covered all. One of the Marines in the bomb dump climbed into two trucks loaded with rockets and drove them away from the one that was exploding.

One unit of eight 500 bombs dropped on a Marine. He was alive and talking, but his legs were flattened from the waist down. When the bombs were lifted, the pain knocked him out. He was taken to a hospital and I don't know if he survived because he was shipped out before I could find out.

I tried to warn the pilots and other officers in the living area to keep their heads down. It did no good. One new officer was shot in the throat from the top of the building he lived in. He was taken to the hospital ship immediately, but died two days later.

Just as day was breaking over the base, with fires everywhere, a Phantom touched down and blew up, adding one more fire to the rest of the night's activities. After the shooting and rocketing stopped, I took a tour of the perimeter. The perimeter at the flight line had three huge fuel tanks burning in front of it.

The bomb dump was in good shape, but there were rockets everywhere. Those remaining in the bomb dump took some casualties and were sent to one of the hospitals. I went back to my command bunker and got all the reports from the platoon commanders.

We had been prepared enough for the attack, had suffered a few casualties in the bomb dump, but did not have anyone breach the line. I went to the CO of the Air Base Battalion and requested to do something about Dog Patch, a small village next to our living area that was presumed to be friendly and benign.

I considered it neither. We took constant sniper fire from Dog Patch and it blocked the fields of fire of all my guns in the living area and most of the bomb dump. I wanted to sweep it and see what was there. I was told no.

Since I couldn't do anything in the way of preventive action, I took my jeep and one of the platoon commanders and gave the guards along the line LAW launchers and showed them in detail how to use them to blow down the hooches of the Vietnamese where the sniper rounds came from. They knew better than I how to use them, but the Vietnamese took interest in the preparations and the number of rounds from the village dropped.

I was instructed to hire a Vietnamese woman as a maid. I had only a bed and locker box, which I kept locked because she was there. She turned out to be a VC sympathizer and took all my pictures of me and my family, as well as everything not locked up. Shortly thereafter, I was informed that I had a price on my head. Thanks to my maid, they had pictures of me in addition to any description she would have provided.

The third night after the attack, things calmed down. I went to bed early, but was awakened by a shock wave hitting the side of my Quonset hut. The blast shook me to my bones, even inside the hut. I ran outside to see what was happening.

There was a mushroom cloud over the harbor. I thought, oh no, they finally did it; they dropped the big one. The mushroom cloud was framed against the moonlit sky. It took me an hour to find out what happened. What had been dropped was a satchel charge into an ammunition ship which went off in one big blast. It left a hole around it and a piece of the bow ten feet long with the anchor chain attached to a piece of concrete located out in the hole made by the ship.

When I got back in the late morning from my perimeter inspection, I found the gunny with a prisoner, taken the night before on the perimeter. He seemed bereft of his senses. I asked him what happened to the prisoner, a VC clad in black pajamas who was clearly an older man.

He said that a VC sapper company had tried to penetrate the south end of the base with satchel charges, probably headed for the flight line or fuel farm.

They reached a point approximately halfway through the barbed wire when they had tripped a flare and the reinforced platoon in front of them had blown them to pieces. The old man was the company commander of the sapper company, which was made up of young women from one village. He was probably related to many of them.

He went crazy on the spot. The American troops acted like they were in shock too, because of what they had done to the young women. The old man in black pajamas was taken, babbling incoherently to the wing headquarters.

The American women in Vietnam were non-combatants and were not in the field. My only experience with an American woman other than nurses, Red Cross workers who stayed near hospitals and headquarters, or my gal buddy that ran the USO at Chu Lai, came one evening. I was driving on my rounds and found a young woman sitting within fifty yards of the perimeter at dusk. She was waiting for an aircraft to come in. I felt immediately protective and stopped doing what I had been doing, checking the runways.

She was the girlfriend of a pilot and knew his aircraft and when it would be returning. I felt that I should stay instead of leaving. She was unarmed. Had she been an armed soldier, I would not have felt as such. I wondered afterward what I would do if women served with us like they did back in States. I think I would have been prone to be protective of them, rather than inclined to do what I was supposed to be doing.

Later, when I did have women in the field, that is exactly how I felt. I put their safety ahead of my objective, time and time again. I don't think I could have functioned during combat situations, unless I completely changed the way I dealt with women.

The TET offensive did not drag on as it did in 1968. Within weeks, we were back to operating on the normal routine of flying and fighting away from the base.

Flight operations at Da Nang were so heavy, I didn't see how they kept from having one accident after another. Vietnamese in Sky Raiders, Air Force pilots in a dozen different aircraft and Marine pilots in A-4s, A-6s, F-4s and RF-4s, as well as all types of transports busied the pattern day and night. I was nearing the end of my tour of duty in Vietnam and wished I was still flying. But instead, I was having to deal with internal problems on the base and with the personal problems of the enlisted men.

Coming from a middle class background did not prepare me for the personal problems that I encountered from some of the enlisted Marines, both black and white. I had no idea how to handle wives who would marry several Marines and collect their allotment checks. All I could do was send the information back to the nearest base.

Families would disappear and the soldiers had no way of locating them. Brothers and sisters would write the Marines expecting them to deal with problems back in the states. Issues that they would not have been able to handle at home, and certainly not from Da Nang. I would refer as many as I could back to the nearest base in the states, but only a few times did I get an answer.

Drugs were so prevalent that I didn't try to locate them. I had so many persons turned in that I was confiscating several ropes a week that were turned in by others. A rope is a three pound coffee can with a single marijuana cigarette rolled up inside. Now I was functioning as a Drug Enforcement Agency rep. Jeezus.

The Freedom Hill R and R center was located some 500 meters from the bomb dump gate. I told everyone that they should not walk that 500 meters alone. One construction worker paid no attention to the guard and did so. We found only a blood trail the next morning, less than 100 yards from our back gate.

Tempers flared among friends for reasons known only to themselves. One Sergeant I had, was to be kept in custody. He got locked up when he threatened the other night duty NCO. He went crazy with no warning, yet sadly was to be discharged in only a day or two.

* * * * *

Early one morning, at seven, I was sleeping. I had landed at daylight in the C-117. I was starkly awakened when I heard bullets going through my hut. I had no idea what time it was and thought we had been overrun. Rolling out of bed, I put on my helmet and my pistol belt and peeked around the sandbags.

A Marine was firing on full automatic with an M-14, spraying all of the buildings in the area. When he was reloading, I ran across the road to the command bunker. I grabbed a shotgun and roused the gunny. My gunnery sergeant, whom I considered my executive officer. We slid down the edge of the buildings to where the shooting was coming from. I didn't want the enlisted Marines to have to shoot one of their own, so the gunny and I got into position to stop him, one way or another.

He had reloaded and was swinging an arc toward me. Now he was at the edge of a building. I had my shotgun aimed on the sandbags with the safety was off. He was now less than fifteen feet away.

I had decided where I was going to pull the trigger. He was swinging an arc and firing on full automatic. I picked a position where I could fire before he began aiming directly at us. Just as I was squeezing the trigger, he ran out of ammunition. The gunny grabbed him by the shoulders and took the rifle away from him as he was reloading.

We took him into custody immediately, checked for casualties, and had him transferred to the Sanctuary for psychiatric treatment. When the report came back from the ship, it said that the Lance Corporal, from Motor Transport, had been trying to kill his company's First Sergeant. He had major psychiatric problems that the war had only exacerbated.

The perimeter of the huge Da Nang base was not nearly as secure as those in the Marine Air Group seemed to think. It became a constant problem convincing the pilots and aircrew that there were continual snipers shooting from Dogpatch and other areas where the perimeter road neared the base.

Usually the air personnel did not spend much time on the perimeter. When they did, they were travelling to the flight line to fly. I was on the perimeter every day and heard the night sentries' stories. Since I couldn't convince the senior officers to sweep Dogpatch, I took some of the excess M-60s that had been taken into our custody and placed them on the line. That simple act stopped the snipers from shooting as much. Just as showing the sentries the LAW rocket launchers had done.

The bomb dump was protected by three rows of concertina wire, a road between the first two and a minefield between the second two. On one of my perimeter checks, when we were driving the road in the minefield, one of the snipers opened up on our jeep, the round going between the windshield and me, and another between the driver and me.

That was after we had everyone prepared and positioned to return the fire. No one could see where the firing was coming from. We were between two rows of mines and had to stay on the road between them. Luckily we didn't get hit, nor did we determine the location of the sniper, and he continued to harass vehicles until after I left.

I was now at the point of being rotated back to the states and another Marine was scheduled to take my place. I was given five days to go to Okinawa and get my uniforms and personal possessions in order that remained at Camp Butler, where all Marines orders were kept.

It only took me an hour or two to get my dress uniform cleaned and ready to wear back to the United States. I spent the remainder of the time sightseeing and visiting with other aircrew who were there from our group. It was a chance to buy some things for my wife and get some clothes for myself, since I was much thinner now than when I came "into country." After the week was up, I got on a C-130 going back to Da Nang. It was loaded with guard dogs trained to be so vicious that only their handlers could get near them.

They were in dog cages, stacked from the flight deck to the top of the big transport. The loadmaster left an aisle open between the dogs and the seats along the fuselage, but the dogs were less than three feet in front of the seats. They snarled and bit at the wire, while urinating and making the back of the transport putrid and uncomfortable.

I would fall asleep and awaken to the gnashing of teeth in front of me on the wire of the cages, where my head had fallen. Finally, I escaped to the flight deck and flew the rest of the way to Da Nang asleep next to the Corporal who was the navigator. Upon landing, I was met by the six by six and taken back to the command bunker. I was no sooner there and immediately was asked to fly a flare drop to north of Hue.

I was in the C-117 before I had a chance to change into my flight suit, and did so in the back of the plane. We had forty flares and were going to the far northwest corner of South Vietnam where Laos and the DMZ all came together. This was about as bad an area as there was. We had lost two A-4Es in that same area when I was flying with VMA-311. I couldn't imagine flying the C-117 there at ninety knots, lighting up the entire sky.

I started realizing why I was picked at the last minute to fly when there were so many others who could have. The Lt. Colonel, an A-6 squadron commander, didn't let me touch the controls on take-off or climb out, as usually was the case. He was flying half unaware of what the plane was doing. Near Hue, while still climbing, the plane went into a left bank and nothing was done to stop it.

I reached for the controls and started to level the wings and the plane commander shouted at me and slapped my hands away from the yoke. I wasn't used to this, having spent most of my time flying my own plane and I gave him a dirty look, but he kept flying, half unaware of what was going on.

When we finally got to our illumination run, he set the plane up to run into Laos and back, instead of setting the plane on a north south run where we would stay in South Vietnam and not cross all the heavy guns in Laos. We then proceeded to drop one flare at a time for the rest of the night.

I had seen so many guns in that part of Laos. When we were flying on our inbound turn, I knew that it was only their lack of desire, or appreciation of the illumination that kept them from making a sieve of the C-117.

I had all the radios and was not allowed to touch the controls one time. I kept the flares going until we were out of them and then told the Colonel to return, as we had completed the mission. He paid no attention to what was going on and yet, I wondered what was the problem.

As we were passing Hue and starting our descent into Da Nang, the plane turned again, and I let it go for thirty degrees before taking the yoke, and having my hands slapped away, this time getting angry and telling him if he didn't want to fly the plane, to let me do it. He said nothing until we were one-half mile from the runway and then gave me the controls to land when I had no feel for the plane.

I bounced two or three times, but made a decent landing and taxied the C-117 to the hangar area and shut it down. I was given a debrief longer than the ones I got in flight training, even though I had flown nearly fifty hours on flare drops.

The next morning, I walked over to where some of the A-6 pilots in the squadron were waiting for the mess hall to open for the noon meal. I asked them about this Lt. Colonel who flew with his mind in neutral and was so willing to criticize the flying and abilities of others. They said I was lucky. They had to put up with it day after day and in addition, some of them still had to fly with him.

During the fifteen months preceding this, I had flown more than 275 missions, in three types of aircraft with wingmen and pilots who ranged in rank from Master Sergeant to General and never had been treated in such a deprecating manner. I was not in Da Nang long enough to follow up on a Commanding officer who was detested by those who flew with him. I cannot imagine flying where the A-6s did. They were required to enter Laos and North Vietnam at night. But I was appalled at having to fly with someone who would act in the cockpit like I saw him act. I would have liked to follow up on his squadron and his career to see what happened to someone whose actions made you wish to be as far away from him as you could.

Chapter 38

I was now the executive officer of my company. The replacement was in and I was showing him how to handle the various aspects of the job. He had no experience handling a ground unit and was going to have to learn most of the problem solving on his own. He was more experienced in the Marine Corps than I was and I felt he would have no problems.

Since he was doing most of what I had been doing, I was scheduled to fly the TA-4F more often. We lost another one when Captain Buffington was shot down in Laos. He was alone and spent the night on the ground in one of the areas where the NVA had no units close by. Luckily, he had been rescued by the Air Force and slept for more than twenty-four hours after he was returned.

Again, I saw the change in a pilot whose experience had gone from the probable to the real. We were running out of planes, and when I was scheduled, usually there was no plane to fly. I saw my name on the flight schedule three days before I was to leave and was surprised to have no idea what type of mission was given the initials ARR. I would be flying from twilight to dawn, unless relieved.

I had no idea who I was flying with, but met the full Colonel at the C-117 along with two enlisted crewmen, a flight engineer, and a first mechanic. The Colonel was just the opposite of the Lt. Colonel I had flown with several nights before.

I started, taxied the aircraft and flew to a position five miles from Da Nang entering into a racetrack pattern. I found out that ARR meant airborne radio relay. We were the antenna for those units in A Shau Valley whose radios could not reach out to their headquarters from the valley, or in other places in the mountains nearby.

The Colonel took the Wall Street Journal, a newspaper a Captain had no need of if he had two children and been married less than four years. He went into the cabin and left me alone, flying three minute legs with a 180 turn at the end of each, while keeping the power back and trying to stay awake.

I was able to entertain myself for an hour looking around at the action on the ground. I spent another two hours playing with all of the ancient radios in the aircraft, listening to Radio Hanoi and tuning in distant places like Cubi Point and Hong Kong on the low frequency radio. Then I just smoldered in the cockpit, wishing I was doing something else.

For four more hours I flew three minutes in a straight line, made a two minute turn and then flew three minutes in another straight line. I was having a hard time staying awake and thought about taking a short tour of Indochina instead of remaining five miles from Da Nang at the closest point and ten miles at the farthest.

In what seemed to be forty hours, the Colonel came back and told me to land. I was already in the Da Nang pattern so dropped my landing gear and did so. I wasn't on the radio frequency that we were passing A Shau to Da Nang so heard nothing but the few planes operating on Da Nang departure on the clear spring evening. I had long ago decided that if I was to keep flying, it would be in jet tactical aircraft and not in the airlines. This one flight, more than any other, made the final decision for me. Whatever I did in life, I was not going to be sitting bored for hours regardless of the pay. This experience had shown me what flying a transport for hours was like.

I went back and slept until noon and packed my personal effects for transshipment to the United States. I had accumulated my own personal jeep, several M-16 rifles, as well as .38 and .45 pistols, all of which I obtained through investigations or were lost and held by me.

I could have taken home a few souvenirs that were in storage in the Intelligence section at Chu Lai, but decided I didn't want any. I turned in the weapons and equipment I had to our armory, rather than risk being court martialed for taking them out of country when I had no interest in shooting them as a civilian, or later, if I stayed in the Marines as I then planned.

I had a lot of papers and other junk to throw away, including old mission cards on my knee pad that dated back to when I came into country. I followed the flight class I had started with on May 9, 1966 because we were together longer than with any other group of pilots.

In Vietnam we were always individual replacements. There had been eighteen Ensigns in the Navy, Second Lieutenants in the Marines and cadets in both the Navy and Marine Corps. All were students with two years of college and paid one-half the pay of a second Lt. until they got their wings and a commission. Of the eighteen, sixteen had remained in flight training.

Of the sixteen, one was killed in Kingsville, Texas when I was in the Naval Hospital, one was killed near Hill 881, one had been captured in A Shau Valley, two were MIA in the DMZ area and two were MIA in North Vietnam. One was medi-vac'd to Japan and the others were still flying. One was never promoted and left behind in the U.S. because he was considered too dangerous to be sent into combat.

I searched for three of those in my flight class who were MIA or captured. None were ever released from captivity. I had come to accept these sorts of things as normal, and put them out of my mind. So many others in the Navy and Marines who had been in other training squadrons, instructors or pilots I had come to know had been killed or captured that it just became something that was part of flying. It made me very aware that I should not push the envelope of my abilities beyond what I knew the limits to be.

I shipped all my personal belongings. Checking the flight schedule, I found I was taking a photographer on a trip of my choice to take pictures for the Associated Press.

I met the Corporal at the aircraft. He was taking pictures with both still and movie cameras. I asked him what the Associated Press wanted, and he said places that had been in the news.

I got him strapped into the rear cockpit and took off to the North. I flew up to Hue, where the Marines had to dig out the North Vietnamese during the 1968 TET Offensive and then went on up into North Vietnam to show him the roads and gun emplacements.

We flew across the DMZ into Laos, where I showed him Khe Sanh and the Ho Chi Minh trail. It was like a super highway compared to when I saw it for the first time.

We flew down the trail at altitudes of 500 feet to 2500 feet. He was able to get some good pictures of the trail and the roads leading into A Shau Valley and beyond.

I continued down to Kham Duc, fifty miles due west of Chu Lai, which was overrun while I was flying with VMA-311. It was still the same as always, a concrete runway, with a large home on the south end. It was where Diem, the former leader of South Vietnam was trying to escape to when killed in the early part of the war.

From Kham Duc, we followed the road into the Chu Lai area, now being used heavily. We were flying only 500 feet above the ground when we came to the first Americal Division fire base above the valley. We flew below it and out into the coastal plain where the Marines were conducting an air strike which he photographed for fifteen minutes. We then flew up the coast, into An Hoa and back to Da Nang. I didn't know what the photos would be used for, but I have seen some of them in the photography of the war used in specials on TV over the years.

I was done flying. We were almost out of TA-4Fs, so I wasn't the only one done flying. I went back to my hooch and prepared to leave the next day. It seemed in some ways I had just arrived at Da Nang a few days before, and in other ways, it seemed like I had been there forever.

At 1000 hours the next morning, I was back at the old French Terminal I arrived at in March 1968 and the same four officers were there that I had flown overseas with. The warrant officer was now a First Lieutenant and the two helicopter pilots had two rows of ribbons, one with a purple heart. The same enlisted men were with us that had been manifested in Los Angeles thirteen months ago but only one-half of them were taking the plane back to Okinawa.

We then flew on to Travis AFB in Sacramento, California. Bizarre because it was exactly where I landed when I returned from my first trip to Vietnam the year before in January, ferrying the six TA-4F aircraft to Da Nang.

Most of them were now gone, shot down in the last fifteen months. As officers, we were seated in the front. Several Navy doctors were now with us. The plane looked so clean and orderly, compared to the dusty and disorganized conditions at the bases I had been to.

As we taxied out of the terminal, I thought there would be some sort of cheer or verbal response by those leaving, most of whom were combat specialties. But the plane was eerily silent as we lifted off of Da Nang's south runway. Phantoms were taking off to the north on the other runway, just as when we had first landed. As we crossed the beach in a steep climb to stay away from the ground fire, I looked back down the coast toward Chu Lai and saw the smoke of activity between.

Remembering how anxious I was when I first saw the coast, the combat inland and the torn up countryside, I found it interesting but there was no anxiety in looking at it now. No feelings at all. I thought I was leaving Vietnam comfortable with war.

Chapter 39

As I exited the plane on the tarmac at Travis, I was glad my wife was not yet there to greet me. I watched as other servicemen ran to greet their families, embracing in arms. I wanted to touch no one. And no one to touch me. I felt I was entering another world. Gathering my bags at the terminal, I checked into a hotel and went to the bar.

I sat there drinking bourbon. Watching clips of the war on the TV news. That was probably the worst thing I could have done. It was two days before I went to the telephone to call my wife and let her know I was back stateside.

"Gene. Thank God you are safe. We were worried we didn't hear from you. All of your family is asking. Where are you?" her voice was high and shrill on the phone. I could tell she had been crying.

"I'm fine. I'm in a hotel, near Travis Air Force Base. I'll rent a car and drive up in a couple of days. The Marine Corps paperwork and all."

"Okay. Be safe. We want to have a big celebration dinner with your family when you get home. We all want to hear about it. And you won't believe how big Michael has gotten."

Michael. The son I didn't even know. My heart was heavy. All I wanted to do was sleep. I sure as hell didn't want to be around too many people. Or talk about Vietnam.

I had leave for a couple of weeks. Besides seeing my sons, being home was torture. I felt like I didn't know my wife at all. Much to her disappointment, I wasn't home long.

I got transferred to the second ANGLICO, which is an Air Naval Gunfire Company attached to an artillery battalion that goes with allies. I served first as an Air Controller and later as a Commanding Officer out of Camp Lejeune. Then I served as a flight instructor with the 10th Marines, eventually being assigned to Camp Garcia, on a small island in Puerto Rico called Vieques.

The injuries I received in the aircraft accident in Kingsville in 1967 made it harder and harder to fly. I had back problems and anxiety issues that made Marine Corps life difficult. I resigned my active duty commission during July of 1970.

My family and I took a trip through Canada on our way back to the west coast, where I was going to look for a job. Before getting halfway across Canada, I called home and found that I had been offered a job as a forester in northern California. I gladly took the job and purchased a home. I was working in some of the most magnificent forests in the world. But I continued to fly with the reserves in Alameda, California.

After several months in the office in Ukiah, California, I started traveling up and down the coast to the timber areas managed by the district for which I worked. Although I was not supposed to do so, I picked up hitchhikers who somehow seemed like myself.

Before long, I realized these were all Vietnam veterans and they all shared the same story. They had, or previously had families and jobs, but were just on the move. When I asked where they were going, they gave a vague answer. If asked where they had come from, the answer usually was from a settled situation from which they appeared to be running.

I was lucky to have had an education before I went into the Marines because I now had a good job, a future and a family. I stopped asking the Veterans about their past and just asked where they had served in I Corps, because that was where virtually all of them had been stationed. I later shortened this to what Marine unit they were stationed within I Corps and was right most of the time.

Over the years, the government hired some of these wanderers but they didn't stay long before moving on. I had seen the same type individuals after World War II when I worked in the fields as a teenager. Because they didn't hold a job long, I thought of them as bums. But now, I found I had too much in common with them to consider them bums. As drifters, I feared they were heading for the skids. I callously thought I was smarter than they were and wasn't going to use Vietnam as an excuse for failure in my life or problems that arose.

Had I been a little more analytical and a lot less critical, I would have noted that I took a job where I was being paid to do just what they were doing; escaping life. My escape involved taking road trips for the Division of Land Management in Northern California. By analyzing my own situation, I would have noted that I was becoming somewhat of a gypsy, always elated to be going to a new place. But once there, excitement turned to discomfort in the new job. I always wanted to leave for the next one. That anxiety, to always be on the move, provoked pressure when there was no pressure.

Then I received a post in Western Oregon. Back in the forest, I walked to work in the morning sunlight and happier than I had ever been before. I was working near the Redwoods and completing surveys along beaches where the whales were migrating up and down the Pacific Coast.

I was working with a forester, Leo Martin, who had been in the woods of the Northwest since 1949. He had 1,000 stories to tell and experiences to share. I learned rapidly and enjoyed this outdoor type of job. It was quite different from flying.

In January of 1971, I experienced my first spell of depression, not even knowing what it was. It went away in two or three days, but came back the same time the next year and lasted longer. I was gone all the time in my job which my wife constantly complained about. But I had been gone more in the Marines than with this position.

Before two years had gone by, I was always on the go. I didn't slow down and was active from the time I got up until the time I went to bed. I didn't return to the interests I had prior to entering the Marines. It felt better to just be alone, as I simply could not relate to my wife. Although I loved my boys, my marriage deteriorated to the point of divorce in 1973. She kept Michael, but Arty wanted to live with me.

The injuries I received in the aircraft accident were now not particularly limiting because I could make my own schedule. But there were weeks at a time when I had to severely limit what I did because of a variety of problems.

As a single parent, I moved near a Veteran's Administration Hospital in Oregon during 1974 with my eight-year-old son. He was able to walk to school and home and became the inevitable latch-key child. The proximity to the hospital made my injuries a minor problem since I could get immediate treatment for them. Despite my new independence, I missed the intimacy of having a woman in my life.

Chapter 40

∞ March, 1974 ∞

While attending a church pot luck supper with my son in tow, I met the love of my life. Joy. Also a single parent, she was there with her own two children. I noticed her from across the room and made my way over to her. She was bending over to wipe away some meringue from her young son's lip.

"Nothing like a good meringue," I stammered out.

"What?" she looked up.

"Just saying there are some great pies here at the pot luck."

"Yes. And he's managed to get them all over his face."

We both laughed. She was small and petite. Only about five foot two. I towered over her.

"I've never seen you here before," she stuck out her hand. "My name is Joy."

"We've just moved here. Well, back here. I grew up in the area."

"Very nice to meet you. And your name?"

"Oh," I laughed. "Gene. Lathrop. This is my son, Arthur." He looked around, embarrassed to have his father talking to a woman. I noticed that Joy was not wearing a wedding ring.

Before the night was over, finding out that she too was divorced, I asked her out for a date. We continued to see each other about once or twice a week. She taught school, so it was mostly on the weekends. She had a charming daughter, named Lisa who was six and an intelligent, artistic son, Scott, age ten. Our children, especially the boys got along great. Often I would take them to the park or for a hike in the woods. Once a week, I took them to swim at the local indoor pool. Our blended family was hitting it off.

During one of our early dates, Joy asked me a question that I didn't answer with the complete truth. It was about the war in Vietnam.

"Hey, can I talk to you?"

"Sure, I am an open book. To you anyway."

"I've been hearing things. About how some Veterans coming home from Vietnam are having . . .well . . . problems."

"Oh. Yeah. I've heard about that too. But not me. I hardly ever think about it at all."

She looked relieved. I took her hand in mine and hoped that the warm fuzzy feelings I was developing for her would make the memories of the war just go away. I couldn't have been more wrong.

One evening, Joy called. We had been going out for several months by now. I knew I had fallen in love with her.

"I hate to bother you, but my car won't start. Do you think you can come over and help me out with it?"

I happily agreed because I wanted to ask her to marry me. I had bought the ring the week before. When I got to the door, she looked very flustered. Her captivating brown hair was muffed up and her hands were dirty from attempting to work on the car. But she never looked more ravishing to me.

"Don't worry. I'll take a look. But only on one condition."

"What's that?" she looked perplexed.

"Follow me out to the car and if I get it fixed, maybe I'll tell you."

Joy followed me out to the car. She was wearing a pair of short blue shorts. Damn her legs looked good. I opened the hood and began to tinker around with the motor.

"When was the last time you changed your oil?"

"I dunno," she smirked.

"And had the oil filter changed or the spark plugs checked?"

Another smirk. "So what were you going to ask me?"

I gave one of the spark plugs that was loose a tweak.

"Just wondering. If I fix your car, will you agree to marry me?"

Her hands flew to her mouth in shock. But she said nothing.

"Well?" I was concerned she was going to say, no.

"Oh, of course I will."

After I fixed the car, we went in and Joy was sitting on my lap. I pulled out the ring and put it on her finger. We went into the den and told our children. They nodded, nonplussed and went back to watching their TV shows.

But her son Scott asked, "We don't have to be adopted do we? I mean, I don't wanna have to change my name."

Joy looked surprised and a bit embarrassed.

"No, sir." I came to the rescue. "We're just blending a family. Just like it has been for the last coupla months. Will that work for you?" I stuck out my hand for a shake.

He gave me his. "Yah, that'll work."

A few weeks after I proposed, Joy had a request.

"Gene. You know I love you, right?"

"I hope so."

"It's just . . . I never want another divorce."

"Me neither."

"We've been going out and to church together for a while. And you like the pastor right?"

"Yeah. Quit beating around the bush, Joy. Out with it."

"I just never want another divorce, that's all. So, if you want me to marry you I want to go to some couples classes. Like premarital stuff. To make sure you believe that I'm the one."

"Counseling?" My jaw tightened. Every pilot I know has an abject rejection to counseling. If you showed any weakness at all you couldn't fly. But I was no longer in the military. She was looking at me with those fascinating brown eyes.

"Pretty please?"

"For you. Okay. But just a few."

"Aw, honey. I love you so much. Thank you, darling."

We continued to do lots of family things together, as well as dates alone. I looked forward to the time that I could have her all to myself. We had great chemistry.

I became a member of the Lutheran church with my son, Arthur. Belonging to the church gave me structure. Something that I was missing. I participated with Joy in the music group, singing in the choir. Our families were all very happy and supportive of our union. Joy was a catch.

We married on March 16, 1975 in the Lutheran church at Rosenberg, Oregon. When I look back at the pictures I laugh. Dressed in my baby blue and black plaid jacket and white turtle neck with matching black trousers, I towered over sweet Joy. She was dressed in a pale blue maxi dress with a laced bodice and short sleeves. On top of her brown hair she wore a matching big floppy hat and carried a single cream colored rose.

I would never forget our anniversary because it was the day that I was involved in the plane crash at Kingsville. Oh well, at least I would remember.

I now had three children for whom to care. My own children were active in sports and did well in school. We developed an active life in the community. I became a council member of the church and later served as president. My wife taught second grade in a small country school about five miles outside Rosenberg. I went back to working as a forester in Rosenberg for the

Bureau of Land Management. We purchased a nice home in a quiet neighborhood. Our family situation was nearly perfect.

I never told Joy, but I was experiencing longer and longer periods of depression, especially during the winter. They scared me because I could not explain them. Not knowing what else to think, I accepted them as normal.

When I returned to the U.S. in 1969, Vietnam always seemed like it happened to somebody else. By 1975, I had little memory of it at all. With my new wife and children, it rarely crossed my mind.

Chapter 41

A lthough I left the reserves when I moved to Oregon, I continued to fly enough locally to keep up my commercial pilot's license remembering the flying well enough. I had a wonderful new family. I was working in some of the most resplendent timberland in the United States. For the next few years, life was bliss. Or so I thought.

The job in the field was not like work. Being a forester and using my education was like exercising on a long vacation interspersed with periods of difficult conditions. Days of firefighting, dealing with trespassers, as well as those who stole timber alternated with quiet days alone in the forest. I now had almost total freedom on how to do my job.

I could work around my injuries without any issues. The physical demands were light because I could stay in the office for a day or two, therefore not having any real problem with them. However in 1980, the pain in my neck and back forced me to move to an office job. It was a promotion which gave me even more freedom and a good future. The management job was a stepping stone to higher positions which would be a value to my family. But I had no idea how much I would miss the solitude of the forest.

Although I was able to be more creative in my new position, the periods of depression started lasting up to thirty days. But then would disappear for another year. I had learned to put up with them like putting up with a headache or any other bother. The charade of happiness I kept up with Joy and my children masked what was really going on. I was so active that when I was in the depressed state, it often passed on its own. The war seemed like some distant memory.

Once in a while, the ex-Marines in our office would get together and talk about Vietnam. But we all admitted that we were talking about something that seemed across a gap in time which was not real. I never had a temper, but on two occasions when I was pressed into a corner by the foolish and angry reaction of another, I simply lost it. Deteriorating into such a rage, I had to leave for fear of losing total control. After each of these situations, I tried to ask myself what was happening.

One afternoon while I was driving home from work, the dam on my emotions cracked and I started crying uncontrollably. By the time I reached home, my eyes were swollen and puffy. Opening the door to home and seeing Joy, I burst into tears.

"Gene? What's wrong darling? What's happened?" Joy had never seen me cry.

"I dunno. Nothing. Everything. I can't explain it." I pulled away from her and went into the bedroom just sobbing. I didn't know it at the time, but Joy's daughter and my son Arty both saw me. Joy told me that they exchanged strange looks like I was a freak.

* * * * *

In January of 1984, we had a new manager take over who was so unpopular that the entire organization unified against him. But I didn't just dislike him. I wanted to kill him. Marines were trained to kill. It was a thought pattern that made me question if I was in my right mind.

One evening I read an article about Vietnam Veterans. The papers told stories about some of the reactions of the Veterans exploding into rage.

"Joy, can you believe this crap?"

"What are you talking about, Gene?" she asked frying up some pork chops for dinner.

"This article is talking about Veterans going crazy. Raging on people and ending up in jail."

"That's terrible. Especially after they served our country."

"Damn straight they did. But how dare they blame the military for their screw ups. Maybe they deserve to be in jail or worse in the loony bins at the VA."

"Gene. If they have problems, they may need help."

"That's just a load of bull, Joy. If they were Marines, they'd deal with it."

Arrogantly, I thought their emotional problems were theirs and not mine. I had dealt with the war. I suffered through being spat at in the terminal when I came home. I knew that Veterans had been called doped-up baby killers. But there were so many of us who were normal, working and doing okay.

"Gene, do you realize that sometimes you have nightmares?"

"No, I don't."

"Yes. I was going to tell you. You do. They wake me up."

"Really?"

"Just about every night. You start tossing and turning. And mumbling things I can't recognize."

It made me think. It made me scared. I knew Joy was worried about me. But we didn't talk about it. Little did she know, but it was about to hit the fan.

Another incident happened at work. Someone had screwed up and lost a report. Hours of data that weren't retrievable and would have to be repeated. I lost it. I started shaking. I was livid. My secretary noticed it and called the boss.

"Gene what's going on?"

This time I couldn't hide it. I had to think fast.

"It's nothing. I've been having trouble with my blood pressure. They think I might have hypertension."

"Oh, are you seeing a doctor?"

"Yeah."

"Gene, you just don't look right. I'm going to call your wife."

"No. Don't. I'll just drive myself home."

"Nope. That's not happening. Janet, get Joy on the phone."

My wife was teaching that day. They phoned her in the middle of the school day. She left work and came and picked me up.

"Gene. What's happening to you? I'm really worried. I want you to see a doctor."

"No. I'm not going to see a doctor."

"But I think something's wrong. You're not sleeping. You're so keyed up."

I will never forget the look on her face. My rage boiled over and I screamed at her.

"Shut the fuck up, Joy. Just shut up. Nothing is wrong with me God damn it."

She burst into tears. I had never spoken to her that way. She cried all the way home. When we got home, the kids knew something was up.

"What's going on?" Scott queried.

"Nothing. Just nothing. Don't worry about it."

I was humiliated. Nothing had ever affected my ability to do my job. Not in the military and certainly not as a civilian. I had to get a grip on what was going on. And what had I done to my Joy?

Other things were happening too. Joy and I would have arguments. She would come home and find me still under the covers, having done nothing all day. But I couldn't talk to her. About any of it. I started spending more and more time away in the forests. I would get over it. It would pass. It always had. I went to the VA clinic, but they told me that nothing was wrong. That the episodes would pass.

But they didn't. Later that week, when Joy came home from school, she was surprised to find me up off the couch. I was in the kitchen fixing dinner for the family.

"Gene. We need to talk."

"Yeah. I know."

She had a brochure in her hand and put it on the table.

"What's that?"

"What I want to talk to you about. You know that I love you. We've both been divorced. And I'm not about to go through a second one. I want us to see a counselor. A marriage counselor."

"No way. Not a freaking shrink."

"Gene, I'm serious. We need help. To cope with whatever's going on. Something's not right," she began to cry.

It crushed me to see her that way. To think that what was going on inside my head was hurting her so much. Reluctantly, I agreed to go. We started seeing a female psychologist who specialized in couples therapy. Thank God no one I knew would report seeing a shrink to the FAA.

Going to a therapist was torture. Not to mention she was female. What would a woman shrink know about war? After several sessions, the therapist put out a theory.

"Gene. Joy. I have a theory about what's going on?"

"Oh yeah? What's that?" my tone was sardonic.

Joy squeezed my leg and gave me a look. The therapist continued.

"Go on, doctor."

"Gene, I've been reading. I think that you're suffering from something called post-traumatic stress disorder."

"PTSD? The crap they're writing about in the paper?"

"Yes."

"No. Not only, no. But hell no."

I got up to walk out. This was it. No more counseling crap. I was a Marine. God damn it. A fighter pilot. A warrior. I didn't have any PTSD. That was just bullshit.

"I'm recommending that you consider going into treatment. With a new program at the V.A. at American Lakes," the therapist continued.

"Joy. Get your purse. Let's go." I got up to leave, but stopped at the door. I was angry because I knew the therapist was right. She was spot on. Suddenly, my machoism disappeared and I burst into tears. Joy came over and tenderly wrapped my towering frame in her delicate arms. It was a moment of tenderness and love I will never forget.

"No matter what I do," I sobbed an eternal river of tears. "Any activity. All I think about is Vietnam," I buried my head in Joy's embrace. It was breakthrough moment. The therapist sat silently. Finally. The secret I had been holding was out.

But over the next few months, things at home got worse. I had so much time on my hands in the forests. All I could do was think. But the peace and solitude of the forests that I had always relished were no cure. Their remarkable beauty that I had loved since I was a boy was fading. It was killing me. Thoughts about Vietnam were coming back. The nightmares were increasing.

All hell broke loose one afternoon. On a day off from work, I was upstairs typing away on my vintage Royal typewriter. But my thoughts were scattered. What if the counselor was right? What if something was completely wrong with me? My weird emotive outbursts were starting to affect our children.

Joy's daughter thought I was weird. With all the crying and emotional outbursts, I don't blame her. She couldn't cope with my irrational behavior. She began spending more and more time at other friends' homes, embarrassed at my emotional outbursts. This only added tension to my relationship with my wife.

Despite ending the therapy sessions with Joy, I was determined to make our marriage work. Like Joy, the last thing I wanted was a divorce.

One day while I was at home, a panic attack hit me. I had taken a nap and awoke to a nightmare. I called Joy at the school.

"Joy. Thank God I got you on the phone."

"Gene, calm down. What's going on?"

"You have to come home right away. I can't stay here in the house alone."

"What?"

"They're coming. To take my mind, Joy. They're coming."

"Who's coming, Gene?"

"The gooks. The fire. They're going to set fire to the house. Napalm it." I didn't realize I was screaming. "Come home. Now."

"Gene. Just calm down. Please." I could hear here crying.

"Joy. What's happening to me? Help me."

"I'll see what I can do, Gene. I'll come home okay. Just stay put."

By the time she came home, the panic attack had subsided. I was on the couch, just crying. I couldn't understand what was happening. I was in the body of someone else. Certainly not Captain Robert Gene Lathrop, USMC.

* * * * *

On January 23, 1984, nearly sixteen years since I had reported into Vietnam, disaster struck. I woke up reacting to a loud noise. On the floor, pressed into a rug to get low enough so the incoming shrapnel would stay above me, I was shouting.

"Incoming. Get down, get down. Incoming."

Joy woke up in the bed screaming. She leapt off the bed and tried to comfort me.

"Gene. Wake up. Wake up. You're having another nightmare. Gene."

But I couldn't hear her voice. I only continued screaming. I could only see red. A tower of flames. I knew we were being attacked. Sweat poured from my brow. I was physically shaking.

My devoted Joy never left my side. She put her arms around me and just held me on the floor until it passed. Thank God Arthur was at school and Joy's daughter and son were spending the night with friends. The next morning, I never felt worse in my life.

For the next few months, I made every excuse possible to not go to therapy. But I had depression and anxiety so bad that I couldn't sleep more than two hours a night. Having been an outpatient at the local Veteran's Administration Hospital, I knew where I had to go. The thought of hospitalization terrified me. I remembered Corpus. But this wasn't physical. The nightmares were continuing. There was one evening that again, the incoming were deafening my ears. This time, I saw flames and felt my flesh burning. Again I was on the floor, drenched in sweat. I finally gave in to Joy's suggestions. I was admitted to American Lakes Veterans Hospital the next day.

Chapter 42

To this day, I don't know if my admission to American Lakes was the right thing to do. Treatment for post-traumatic stress disorder was new. As I parked my old pick-up in the parking lot and prepared to enter, I shook with trepidation.

When I was admitted for that eleven week session, they started me on medications which knocked me on my ass. I vacillated between periods of lucidity and periods where the world just seemed like some hazy movie and not real.

American Lakes was a gorgeous stucco group of buildings built on the shores of the crystal blue waters of the lake. There were tall, gorgeous pinion pines and junipers, much like the forests where I served as a ranger. But the architectural beauty of the facility itself was lost when one knew what was happening inside.

Treatment in group sessions was abominable. They wanted you to talk and share, yet I could barely feel my tongue, which was thickened with whatever drugs were inside me. I later found out it was Thorazine, a powerful sedative.

Everybody there seemed to be just like me. At one time, well employed, many divorced and most of us unable to remember specifics of the war. But in group, they were relentless. They would ask and ask and ask. They were going to blast the war out of you, one way or another. A barrage of questions that would get you so angry that you'd let down your defenses and let the memories come back. This of course was supposedly to help you deal with the war.

In those sessions, there was rage. Tears. Lots of tears. Grown men crying. Balling like babies. It was hard to watch. And even harder to engage. Most of the time, I wouldn't speak up much, but I did start to write. They taught us that one way to deal with the anger was to put your feelings down on paper if you couldn't talk about them. That seemed to work for me. So I wrote down all kinds of things, to just get them out. But then I would throw them away after the therapists read them. It was an expenditure manager.

For the guys that wouldn't talk or participate at all, they would strap them down on gurneys and take them to a room down the hall. I would hear them screaming. And then hear nothing at all. I knew that they were getting electro-shock therapy, like in that movie with Jack Nicholson, *One Flew Over the Cuckoo's Nest*. I wrote and talked because I'll be damned if I was gonna let someone shock the hell out of my brain. No fucking way.

Joy was not allowed to visit. Not seeing her nearly killed me. I was a mess. The first couple of times I talked to her over the phone, I just burst into tears. I must have sounded like a wreck.

"It's all coming back. The war. I just want to go home, Joy."

"I know, darling. And you will. When you get better."

"The missions. The madness of it. We were never gonna win that fucking war. Why were we even there? Face. They were only trying to save face."

"Who, Gene?"

"The gooks. They used their own people. Families. Kids. Just shields," I tried to explain it all to her through sobs.

"One guy got so upset, he committed suicide. It's bad, Joy. I don't know if I can do it. Take me, home." I heard her voice tremble. I knew she wanted to be supportive. My gorgeous, sweet Joy. I missed her so much. I'm sure she was thinking she was married to a nut job. A nut job in the looney bin.

The only way I was able to stay completely sane was that I often cheeked some of the meds. Had I taken all of what they wanted me to, I would have been nothing more than a zombie. Tranquilizers. Anti-anxiety meds. Anti-psychotics. Before cheeking them, sometimes during my telephone calls with Joy, I could barely talk. My words were slurred and my tongue thick as a bovine's. About halfway through the treatment, I had made enough progress in their eyes by jumping through enough hoops to score a weekend trial release. It was bliss because it was going to coincide with my son Michael's graduation.

At first I was excited to be granted permission to get back in my old truck and drive to Eugene, Oregon for the ceremony and party. My head was fuzzy though from the meds. But there was no way I was going to let any of the doctors know that. I was determined to make it on my own. Not only was I going to get to see my son, but my beloved Joy. It had been weeks.

But coming home temporarily to the stigma of a mental hospital admission was humiliating. I felt like people just stared at me, like I was a freak. My children thought I was a bizarre, changed and different. During the graduation ceremony, I found it hard to relate to the gaiety of the celebration with family. I couldn't relate. All I could think about was Vietnam. I wanted people to understand about the war. Especially what had happened to me.

Chapter 43

∞ May, 1984 ∞

The last thing any parent wants to be is an embarrass-ment to one's children. In May of 1984, I became exactly that. It should have been a time of celebration. My estranged son Michael was graduating from high school. I had missed so much time with him. I wanted in this moment of celebration to make it up to him.

When I divorced, Michael who was born while I was de-ployed to Vietnam, decided to live with his mother. Why shouldn't he? She was all he knew. I tried to stay in contact with him. But we had always been distant. He knew nothing of the love of children I had been able to give to Arthur, Scott, and Lisa as well as their children.

Through the generosity of my ex, Janet, I had been extended an invitation. It was probably too soon after my admission to American Lakes and my ongoing treatment for PTSD to be around anyone else but immediate family. I was still heavily medicated and trying to figure everything out.

The event didn't go as Joy and I planned. My mind was still screwed up with all the drugs. Thorazine. Xanax. Buspar. I was often times talking about things that didn't make sense.

My affect was placid enough, but evidently, I appeared out of it. Like some kind of drugged caricature. Not a Vietnam Veteran. Not an attack pilot. Not a warrior.

I was seen in the few conversations I could manage, as a sad, drugged, pathetic individual. My speech, as Joy later informed me, was sluggish. In the few words I managed to utter, all I was focused on was talking about the horrors of Vietnam.

I wanted nothing more than to convey the pride and honor that I felt for Michael's achievement. His graduation from high school. All I wanted was for him to see that I was there for him. I had missed so much time with him. But that was not to be the case.

"If you knew he was in this kind of condition, I can't understand why you brought him here?" Janet disparaged. "Is he high on something?"

Joy was silent. She didn't know what to say.

"This is a life changing moment for Michael. All he wanted was to reach out to his father."

"I'm so sorry. Gene thought the same. He wanted to be here, to show his support," Joy tried to defend.

"Well, he's done just the opposite. Look at him. He's a drugged out crazy. He barely speaks to anyone and when he does, he's doing nothing but spewing all that rhetoric about Vietnam."

"I know. I apologize."

"He can't even focus on the event of the day, his own son's graduation!" Janet slammed down some plates near the elaborate cake which she had ordered honoring our son.

I didn't know what to say. Joy tried her best to deflect Janet's remarks. I wanted to speak up too, but knew better. Another display of emotion would only make things worse. My thoughts and feelings were flat due to the drugs. I just wanted my son to know who I was and that I loved him. Was that so much to ask?

That awkward experience, the inability to relate to my own son, on a remarkable occasion, his graduation, just killed my soul. The power of the drugs for my treatment of PTSD had just eliminated any possibility of a relationship with my own son. I was horrified. Humiliated. I didn't know when the opportunity would again arise for me to stand up as Michael's father.

I tried to talk to Joy in the car on the way home. "So how do you think that went?"

"It was nice. You should be so proud of Michael."

"I am. But I don't think he was proud of me."

"Oh?" she remarked innocently. "What makes you think that?"

"I think he was embarrassed."

"I think we were all embarrassed," she admitted.

"Was it that bad?"

"It was pretty awful. But Janet is Janet. I am sure Michael understood. Don't you think?"

"No. The way he responded to anything I said. So superficial. He doesn't even know who I am."

"I agree. He has spent too much time with his mother, I am sure he doesn't. The question is . . . what can you do to change that? What can you do to make a difference in the future?"

"Wait. Give it time?"

"Give it time, Gene. He knows you love him. Just give your treatment time and let him see you the next time when you feel more like yourself. You know?"

She was right. Again. Time. I would give it time and then, hopefully, Michael would understand. After bringing Joy home, I reluctantly kissed her goodbye, got in the truck and drove back to finish the therapy I had started.

Chapter 44

The eleven week treatment at American Lake changed me. Forever. The treatments opened up a flood of emotion which I'm not sure was a good idea. I was really angry at the government, the war, for what was happening to me. I couldn't control it. Once the quiet one, now no one could shut me up. I began to tell tales. A monologue of them. According to Joy, over and over and over.

I wanted to share the flood of memories with the people that I loved, so that they could relate and not judge me. The stories just started pouring out. I told them to anyone who would listen. It made holidays difficult and uncomfortable for my family.

During Thanksgiving, the first one after I got out of American Lakes, I told my sister about what had happened in Vietnam.

"Susan, you just don't understand what it was like. The bombings. The napalm over villages. Some of what the media reported was right. We were baby killers. Killing villagers and children."

"Stop. Gene. I don't want to hear about it. Not again. Just cut the turkey, Gene." She handed me a knife. "Just cut the turkey."

"Yeah, Dad," piped in Arthur. "Don't you get it? No one wants to hear about Vietnam. None of us."

Arthur didn't realize it at the time. But that statement. Coming from the son that I loved so. The one that I thought understood and respected his father. It crushed me.

A demon had been unleased. They said I had to get it out, if I didn't, the nightmares wouldn't go away. People had a right to know about the overall effect of the atrocities of war. I didn't realize how bad it was until I heard Joy talking on the phone.

"Yeah, I guess he's better. I don't really know. It's like a dam was broken. My once introverted husband just can't stop talking."

Pause.

"I know. At church. At every pot luck. The holidays. Especially when we are with family. Vietnam. Vietnam. Vietnam. Everywhere we go. It's always in his mind and always on his tongue."

Pause.

"I don't know what to do. It's driving me insane. I'm just trying to be patient with him. You know?"

Pause.

"But I love him. I need to stand by him. After all, I'm the one who made him go."

Pause.

"I know. I know. He's a different person. He's angry about what happened to him over there."

I winced at her words, but knew they were true. I was angry. Very angry.

Especially about one particular mission that I now believed was the root cause of it all. My Lai. The story of the My Lai massacre came to light during the 1970s, when an investigative journalist, Seymour Hersh broke a story after interviewing Lt. William Calley. Calley had been charged with the murder of 109 Vietnamese civilians. Shortly after that, a second investigation was initiated to examine the cover-up and possible war crimes committed under the leadership of Lt. General William R.

Peers. Of all the officers charged during the inquiry, only Calley was convicted. All of the other top brass charged were acquitted. But Calley was their scapegoat. He was sentenced to life in prison, however only served three and a half years, being pardoned by Nixon.

Although I had heard about My Lai at that time, I paid no heed. In 1970, the war was over for me. Or so I thought. But now, I began to remember all of the missions I flew. All the napalm I dropped, especially on that one eerily empty village. Did I, as a pilot have something to do the My Lai cover-up? I wondered, as I poured over my pilot's log book. Reviewing mission after mission. Hour after hour. Night after night. I pulled maps. Researched the geography. Plotted coordinates.

"Gene, come to bed. It's two AM. I have to work."

"In a minute, Joy. This is important."

I ignored the fact that I was frustrating the hell out of her. But then, one night I found it.

"Oh, my God. Oh, my fucking God. No."

"Gene," Joy shot out of bed. "Gene. What's wrong?"

"It was me. Oh, God," I sobbed uncontrollably. "It was me. I napalmed that village."

"What village, Gene?"

"My Lai. Oh, God. Oh, God. Oh my God." I sunk to my knees.

"Christ almighty, Gene. Thank God the children aren't home. Come here," she reached around me. "Come here." She held me for the longest time as I continually sobbed. I couldn't let go of the log.

There it was in my personal scrawl in the blue leather log book. October 8 and October 9, 1968. The dates and the coordinates of the mission matched. Bravo 5 715 789.

It was one of my napalm missions. I was one of the two pilots involved in napalming the villages of My Lai. In this case My Lai IV. In carrying out my duties. My mission without question. I dropped my napalm. It must have been to cover up the controversial military screw up of the massacre. As a Marine pilot of honor, courage and commitment, I never questioned my orders. I did my duty. But looking into that log book, figuring out the dates. Realizing that I could have been one of those pilots, I never got over it.

Chapter 45

My Lai became a cause. It involved Lt. Calley. I believed, as many others did, that Calley was being use as a scapegoat. The government had pinned the entire My Lai massacre on his shoulders and he was court-martialed. Despite his release, it just wasn't right. So, I began a writing campaign. To my congressmen. Both Senators and my U.S. Representatives. High up military personnel in the Pentagon. My fellow veteran Marine superiors. Anyone I could think of that would listen. The Washington Post. The New York Times. I even wrote Calley in prison.

Click. Click. Click went the keys of my vintage Royal type-writer. I wrote letter, after letter, after letter. With the information I had pieced together, someone would take action.

I couldn't stop thinking about it. At home. When I was up in the forestry tower. How could the government let one person fall for something that obviously the higher ups ordered? I had the data. I knew. I couldn't stop talking about it either.

Pacing back and forth in the hallway, I wore out the carpet between where I typed and the stairs. Joy just left me alone. But I pestered her while she cooked, cleaned and tried to survive my obsession.

"Joy, do you realize that every plane involved. Every plane somehow or another had accidents? Weird fuel things. Right before I left."

"Accidents happen in planes, Gene. You've said that yourself."

"No. Seriously. It's My Lai. Everyone involved has somehow met some untimely end. It's only a matter of time."

At the time, I was taking Nardil, a potent MAO inhibitor for depression. Xanax, a benzodiazepine for anxiety and Buspar, another anti-anxiety agent. But none of them were working. I was possessed. I had to find someone to listen. I had the data proving that others were involved. The cover-up was ridiculous.

* * * * *

One afternoon, while I was on forestry duty, the home phone rang. Joy answered it.

"Hello? Lathrop residence." It was a voice she had never heard.

"I'm looking for Captain Robert Lathrop."

"I'm sorry, Gene's not at home. He's on forestry duty."

There was initial silence.

"This is Lt. Calley. Tell Lathrop I have a message for him."

Joy said she started shaking. Why was he calling at our home?

"Just tell him this. The government didn't want the details out."

"The details. Okay. I'll relay that message."

There was a click. Joy was still tremoring and nervous when I got home. It really freaked her out. But Calley never called back. And I never returned the phone call.

I was becoming more and more frustrated with the lack of response to my letters. The government officials never responded. The press essentially told me to be quiet, that I offered nothing new.

Was I being quieted? Did they want my information squelched? What if the house was being bugged? I got up from the typewriter and began to sweep the house for bugs. I looked under phones. Behind picture frames. Under beds. I was in Joy's daughter's room when all hell brook loose.

"What are you doing?" she asked as she entered her room after school. Her face was contorted into a look of abject disgust.

"Sweeping the house for bugs," I defended. "Bugs. Listening devices. But instead I found these," I glared at her, tossing some instant polaroid photos onto her bed. They were of her and a young man cuddling.

"Where did you get those?"

"Under you bed. Hiding something?"

"How dare you?" she raged. "How dare you violate my privacy. Get out of my room."

"It's my house. Mine and your mother's."

"But it's my room. You have no right to go through my things."

"Since when did you get a boyfriend?"

"That's none of your business."

"The hell it's not. If he's going to date you, can't he come to the house and at least introduce himself?"

"Why would he want to? To come meet some kook my Mom married?"

The words stung. About that time, hearing the shouting and commotion, Joy came up the stairs.

"What is heaven's name is going on?"

"The weirdo you're married to was going through my things."

"Oh, dear. Gene, why?"

"I was sweeping for bugs when I came across those," I replied pointing to the snaps on the bed.

"That's just Josh Mayfield. He's in band with her at school. You remember the Mayfields, don't you?"

"It sure looks like they're way more than friends."

"She's sixteen. They've been dating."

"So you knew?"

"Yes. So what?"

"But I'm the man of this house," I made my case to Joy.

"But you're not my father. Thank God." Lisa's words cut deeply. She stormed out of the room. "I'm going to Deb's."

"Overnight?" Joy asked.

"Maybe forever," she glared at me with hatred.

I had really blown it. However, I was furious that I had been left out of the loop of the goings on with my own family. I heard the front door slam and Lisa's car screeching out the driveway.

Joy turned to me with a forlorn look on her face. "Gene, we need to talk. You've got to continue the work. With a psychiatrist. Or a therapist or something."

"I'm done with all that. I told you I'm never going back."

"Then let's go together. You can be an outpatient."

"No."

"Look. I love you, but you've got to do something. Or risk losing everything. Do you understand?" Her lip was trembling.

Looking at her, I did. I couldn't lose her. Not now. My head initially hung down, but I raised my eyes to look at hers. That sweet, but pained face.

"Fine. I'll start seeing someone at the VA. But by myself."

I started back with outpatient therapy sessions once a week. I hated them, but I was willing to do anything to save my marriage. Joy was my everything. She's all I had left.

Chapter 46

∞ Spring, 1986 ∞

In order to survive my craziness, Joy started seeing a therapist too. I was such an ogre, I didn't know how she put up with me. She was still teaching full-time. I was still obsessing over Vietnam. But once I got onto an idea, I couldn't let go. My most productive times were at the typewriter. Unfortunately for Joy, they often consisted of incessant pecking on the keys into the wee hours of the night.

I was still working for the forestry service, barely holding on to my job. There would be times at work when I got caught with my head down on the desk. The psychotropic drugs were taking a toll on how my brain worked. Certain memories were becoming fuzzy. The drugs were mainly to keep me calm, from going off on someone.

Sometimes, Joy would offer me suggestions on how to cope by dropping little hints in our conversations.

"Gene, you know what I heard in my session?"

I would often just ignore her.

"The experts say that two things really help calm the PTSD. Talking about what happened. And God knows you're good at that. But also hanging around other people who have gone through the same thing. You know, like at the VFW."

"I'm not going to a smoky, nasty VFW. You know I hate being around crowds of people."

"Well, maybe you could look up some of the people from your squadron."

"Maybe."

"Here, a guy left his number for you."

I looked down at the piece of paper. It was a phone number with the name Peter Erenfeld on it. Erenfeld. He had been in VMA-311.

"When did he call?"

"The other day, when you were out on BLM duty."

Erenfeld. Wonder where he was? What was he doing now? Was he freaking out too? It wouldn't hurt to at least look him up. I took her suggestion and phoned the next day. I found he was working out of an insurance office in Portland, Oregon. I cold called him and told him that I would stop by during the week.

There was that photograph I remembered him having me take. With the combat helmet, the bullets and that cigar that he always had in his mouth. We were different kinds of Marines to be sure. But Marines were Marines. We were both veterans of the same war. Flew the same planes and the same missions.

*   *   *   *   *

Several weeks later, while on business for the BLM, I drove over to a typical office type building. I was wearing my usual outfit, my boots, my black rabbit felted cowboy hat, a leather belt with a buckle I had won in my youth, a red plaid shirt, and my pair of aviators. Peter was dressed in a light blue dress shirt, tie with a Marine insignia tie-tack and slacks. Greeting me, he stuck out his hand.

"Gene, longtime no see. Come on in Tomcat. How've you been?"

I knew Joy hadn't told him, at my request, about my PTSD or hospitalization.

"I've seen better days," I managed to get the words out. The drugs had kicked in and my tongue felt thick.

"Oh, yeah man? How's that?"

"Have a little bit of PTSD that's been bothering me."

Peter gave me a strange look. "I think we all kinda have some. How bad?"

"Bad enough. Spent some time up at American Lakes. But I got out. They've got me on some meds."

"How about some coffee?"

"Coffee'd be good. Black with a little sugar."

He had his secretary bring us some. I felt like he was staring at me. Like I was strange or something. His secretary did too.

"So do you ever think about 'Nam?" I asked him.

"Not much. Too busy getting back into life. I started this insurance business. Doing pretty well. Life's moved on. You know the Tomcats have a reunion."

"Oh?"

"Yeah. Down in Pensacola. You should come. It's great to hang out with the guys."

"Scooter pilots?"

"Yeah. And some others too. VMA-311 is still going strong. They're still flying the A-4. But the M series now. Can you believe that?"

"Hmm. Gotta love the scooter."

"Really, Gene. You should try to make it."

"I'm not a big socializer. Like keeping to myself mostly. Out in the forests."

"Yeah? Joy said you were working for the Bureau of Land Management."

"Yep. I like being out in wilderness. By myself. Lots of time to just relax. Get away from thinking about My Lai. The gooks. That was a screwed up war, man. Really messed up. Do you realize that the government tried to cover up a lot of that baby killing that people call it? How much napalm did you drop? We wasted thousands."

Just then his secretary returned with the coffee. Her face was contorted into one of disbelief. I could tell that Peter, too, was uncomfortable talking about Vietnam.

"So how's life with your new wife, Joy? She seemed really nice over the phone."

"Great. Yep. Well, I gotta go. Nice talking with you." I could feel my anxiety kicking in. So I pulled out my trusty prescription bottle and popped two Xanax.

"Do you take a lot of medication?" he asked.

"Enough."

"Are you safe to drive, Gene? I can call someone."

"Heck no. I do it all the time. I'll be fine." I got up and tripped over part of the leg of the chair, but caught myself. Joy told me later that right after I left, he called her. Seems he was worried and thought I was totally wasted and not safe to drive. So much for seeing other veterans. It would be quite some time before I did that again.

Chapter 47

∞ Fall, 1989 ∞

One of my favorite antiques was an old hunting rifle that I had used as a boy up in the mountains with my father. It was rusty and sometimes required oiling. I would take it apart, clean out the barrel and re-load it with shells. I got distracted waving to my neighbors who were out taking a walk. It accidently went off, shooting me in the gut.

The neighbors heard the loud bang and came running. I grabbed my gut as the blood was running through my fingers.

"Gene. Gene, are you okay?' they looked horrified.

"Yah," I swallowed hard. "Damned thing just went off."

"We're calling an ambulance."

"Nah. Just drive me."

"It looks pretty bad. We're calling the ambulance."

Just as I was being loaded into the ambulance, Joy was driving up after school.

"Oh my God, what now?" she said running toward the flashing lights.

"Gene's rifle went off," the neighbor explained.

"Good golly. Did he shoot himself?" Joy cried out.

"No. No. Nothing like that. We were taking a walk and saw him cleaning it."

"I'm sure it was just an accident," the other neighbor explained.

I spent a few of days in the hospital. Luckily, I had just grazed my small intestine and they were able to suture it back up. I drove the nurses crazy pestering them about when I could go home. I walked the halls at all hours of the night with my IV pole. I hated hospitals and needed to get out. Joy brought them muffins and brownies to make up for my bad behavior.

The more medication they gave me, the worse I got. One day when Joy came to visit, she found me on the floor with no clothes on. My hospital room door was wide open with my ass flapping in the wind. Joy was horrified. That incident bought me a day or two in the psych unit because the med/surg nurses complained that I was manipulative and too difficult to manage on a normal unit. During that time, I wasn't nice to Joy at all. I wasn't nice to anyone. I wanted out.

In response, they just gave me more drugs. I was so loaded up on tranquilizers, Joy said I couldn't even put a spoon to my mouth to feed myself. Family that attempted to visit were embarrassed by my condition. Clearly, medical teams still didn't know how to deal with patients that had PTSD. We were just drugged and classified as 'difficult.'

It was Joy who finally rescued me. She went to the nurse's station and demanded to see the psychiatrist in charge.

"Please call my husband's doctor. He's being over medicated. He can't even feed himself."

"Dr. Richards has gone home for the day."

"I don't care. Call him up."

"He'll be back to round in the morning."

"You're not hearing me," I heard Joy's voice raise. "I want to see the doctor who is on-call then. This has got to stop"

She wasn't going to give up. Gotta love that spunk. Finally, the nurse acquiesced and the psychiatrist on call was paged. I was enjoying listening to Joy go to bat for me.

"I want all these medications stopped. Do you hear me? My husband's gorked out of his mind."

"Mrs. Lathrop, please calm down."

"No I won't calm down. He came in here because of a gunshot wound. He doesn't have mental problems."

"His behavior says otherwise."

"Have you lost your own mind?" she was on a roll. "My husband doesn't normally act like this. You have him so drugged up he can't control his own bodily functions!"

"Mrs. Lathrop, please try to calm down."

"No, stop saying that and listen. He has PTSD. He isn't crazy."

"We know he has anxiety. That is why we pre-scribed the drugs to get him to relax."

"PTSD isn't treated that way. Not anymore. Look it up in your journals. You're over medicating. I want it to stop, do you hear me? Now."

Her anger then turned to tears. I could hear her sobbing outside my room. But it had an effect on the doctor. He discontinued all the sedatives I was being given and wrote orders for me to be discharged in the morning.

Joy brought me a set of clothes. All of mine were soiled. I took a shower, was allowed to shave with an electric razor and combed my hair. Dressed in my pressed slacks and blazer, regular clothes, the nurses couldn't get over how different I looked. Far from the pathetic naked man on the floor. My dignity was partially restored.

When I got home, I was enraged. I spent more time writing letters to my congressmen. To government officials at the VA. To newspapers and news agencies. I was on a mission to bring attention to how Vietnam veterans were being treated. I wanted to inform them about PTDS. I wanted give them more infor-mation about My Lai.

Colin Powell, as has now come to light, was one of the top ranking officers involved with the investigation into My Lai. At the time, he was just a young Major. I believe Powell to be a good and honest person. But to save his own career, I think he did what he was told by the higher-ups. He whitewashed it. That's what seems to have happened. I believe it would have come out too, had his run for the presidency panned out.

What became clear to me more than anything else, was that the idealistic values and principles which we supported when going to war, were really nothing more than politically based objectives. Unlike World War II, during which there was a true cause, the Korean and Vietnam wars were about fighting for political objectives. I probably wasted months and months writing those letters to government officials and the press. I finally just gave up.

Taking the drugs which were intended to help my condition, made what was true and not true become blurred. Sometimes, I was sure things had occurred. But Joy would point out that they hadn't. It was very confusing. It stunned me when one evening she confronted me about what clearly were delusions.

"Joy, I am telling you. All my work. All that research was finally going to pay off."

"Gene. Stop it. Just stop it. There is no way that CBS was going to pay you a million dollars for an exclusive interview about My Lai."

"No, I'm not making this up."

"Honey. I just don't think it's possible."

"But she called. Connie Chung's assistant called the house. It was all a go, till they pulled it."

"Who, Gene? Who pulled it?"

"CBS. I'm sure it was the whole cover-up crap. The Feds were afraid at what would come out."

I know Joy didn't believe me. The disappointed look on her face startled me. Was I really losing it? Is that why family didn't want to come around? Even my own kids. My own father didn't want to hear about it. Lisa, Joy's daughter and husband were reasonable. So I tried telephoning them several times. Surely, they would back me up. They'd believe what was coming out in the newspapers.

"And please stop being a pest to poor Lisa. Quit phoning."

"I am not a pest!" I fired back.

It was so embarrassing. I couldn't stand it. I grabbed a backpack and stuffed in some clothes. I was going to take some time. I needed to get out in the forests, to just think.

"Where are you going?" Joy cried out.

"I don't know. But away from here. It's bad enough that my own father thinks I'm crazy. And now you. I won't be a pest to anyone."

I got in the truck and just drove. To where it all started, Walla Walla. I parked out by the old airfield. Where I had first seen the crash. I hated living in suburbia. I needed to get out. It was suffocating me. I made a commitment to stay in therapy to Joy. That I would try to do. But we had to make a change.

After driving home, I decided I would focus my energy in a different direction. I always felt I needed to do something. There were things in the neighborhood that needed attention. So I joined the neighborhood association. I knew quite a bit about land and there were erosion issues with some of the poorly planned drainage ditches. Taking on various causes, I went door-to-door to the neighbors with petitions.

But that didn't last long. Pretty soon, the neighbors were complaining to Joy about my stories. Some of them even told me they didn't answer the door, because they were afraid of me. Seriously? I even got into a battle of verbal obscenities with one of our neighbors who, believe it or not, was also a Vietnam vet. He was just as stubborn and hard-headed as me.

The concern from neighbors was probably because of another event that occurred in our garage. I was looking for some maps that had been packed away. I knew they were in one of the plastic storage bins on the shelf but I couldn't find them. Before you knew it, I was screaming my head off. Tossing around tools that clanked loudly. I kicked over one of the kids' bikes they had left behind.

One of our helpful neighbors came over and knocked on our door. Joy answered.

"Joy, we're so glad you are okay. We heard the commotion."

"What commotion?" she was used to my tantrums.

"We were worried about you. That Gene . . . well that you were okay."

Joy's eyes turned dark and her lip became terse. "I am perfectly fine. Perfectly. And so is Gene. He would never hurt me," she snapped and closed the door. She came out to the garage and I could tell something was amiss.

"What've I done now?"

"Believe it or not. Nothing. It's just our nosey neighbors that can't mind their own damned business."

It was rare that I ever heard Joy cuss. It was kind of sexy really. But I knew she was upset. Just then, I spotted the box.

"There it is. Jeezus. I thought I would never find it."

Joy looked around at the mess I had made in the garage. Ehh, so what? It wasn't like I couldn't clean it up.

* * * * *

Eight years after my hospitalization at American Lakes, there was a straw that broke the camel's back at work. One day, at my forestry job, I had another 'spell.'

The room started spinning. I couldn't focus on the reports I was reviewing. When I stood up from my desk, I tripped and fell to the ground. My secretary came running into the room.

"Agent Lathrop. Agent Lathrop?" my secretary called, shaking my shoulders.

As I returned to consciousness, I could see through blurry eyes that the whole office was surrounded around me as I lay on the floor. My supervisor had called Joy.

"Mrs. Lathrop? This is Special Agent Baxter with the BLM. It seems that Gene, well he's had another episode at work."

"Is he okay? Did you call an ambulance?"

"No. It seems to have passed. He is more awake now and sitting in a chair. But, I have to tell you. I'm worried. He's just . . . not right."

"I see."

"Today, before it happened, he was confused. Just not making any sense. Sometimes, I find that his head is down on his desk."

"Oh, dear."

"I'm . . . well, we all are worried about him. Maybe you should come pick him up?"

I heard that out of his mouth as I approached the door. I held the door frame to steady myself. "Look, Baxter. I'm fine. Probably just some hypoglycemia. I forgot to eat lunch. That's all. No big deal."

"Gene. It is a big deal. And it's not the first time. We are worried about you. I've phoned your wife. She is on her way to come get you."

"I really wish you wouldn't have done that. I can drive myself. I'm fine."

"Agent Lathrop. I beg to disagree, this time."

But I was determined to drive home myself. I was a fucking pilot for Christ sakes. I picked up my briefcase and made my way to my trusty pickup.

I was given the next two days off with pay. But before I had a chance to return, the big boss phoned. I was offered early retirement from the forestry service. The job I loved. The escape. It was now all gone. The one thing that was helping me hold it together. The forests. My peace. My solitude. I spent the next few days in bed. In the dark. I just wanted to give up.

Chapter 48

The break I needed from the disaster that was becoming my daily existence finally came from Joy. It was early in the afternoon when she opened the blinds to our bedroom to let in some light.

"Gene. Hey, honey. It's Joy. I have something to show you." She started rubbing my back. "I think you'll like it."

"Go away. I just want to sleep."

"Not this time, Marine. It's time to rise and shine. Come on. You'll want to see this."

"What?"

She spread out some fliers over the bed. Real estate fliers.

"I have an idea. The kids are grown. This place is just too big. I've gotten some fliers from a small country real estate place out near the school. There's several really nice farms out there. I think it's time for a change."

"A farm? You'd be willing to be a farm girl?"

"I've always liked the country, you know that."

"And what about this place?"

"Suburban real estate it hot. Let's sell it!"

I took a look at the brochures. Rolling hills. Barns. Acreage. Like the farm where I grew up. A tear formed in the corner of my eye.

"I think it's a great idea."

"You do?" Joy sounded surprised.

"Yeah. Let's get the hell outta here."

We spent the next few weeks visiting various different properties and getting our home ready for sale. It didn't take long. We got a great offer and closed the deal. Within a few weeks, we were packing up and preparing to move to our farm in Sutherlin, Oregon.

I had an endless list of 'to do' things. Equipment to buy. Livestock to see. I wanted a horse. A solid one. I scoured country estate sales for tack, saddles and grooming equipment.

We moved to an old farm house on twenty acres. It was around summer, which worked out great, as Joy was off on summer vacation. She was a superb decorator and together, we went to many country sales to pick up antiques and nick knacks to outfit the place.

The farm house was warm and cozy. It had a huge stone fireplace. Knotty pine floors, which we had refinished. Small enough to manage, yet giving us both room to do our own thing. I felt so happy.

I loved the thought of having a horse again. I worked on the barn to make two decent stalls, a tack room, and feed room. For the first time in years, I felt like myself.

Scouring the ads from the local paper, I finally found the horse of my dreams. I couldn't wait to get up in the morning to go out and see my gelding. Standing at sixteen and a half hands, he was magnificent.

He was a radiant bay with a jet black mane and tail which I named Solomon. I would brush his mane and tail until it was silky smooth. Pick out his feet. Run the brush along his back. Smell the horsey smell of his coat. Then saddle him up and take him out for a trot even before Joy was awake. He was my silent warrior. My wingman.

Joy got the house in order before school started. We were close enough that I could still go to the required 'therapy' sessions. For a while, the distractions of a new life, a new place staved off the PTSD. Thank God.

When I wasn't on the horse, I kept up with issues related to the BLM. The forestry service was having problems with extinction of the spotted owl. With my background and training, I began spending more time at the Penrose Library at Whitman College. I drew out maps and made all kinds of plans writing up a proposal to save their extinction. I was pleased with my work.

Driving to the Land Management office, I presented my findings. With my experience and knowledge, surely they would benefit from my work. I went by every couple of days to see what they thought. Little did I know, but they tossed all of my work in the garbage.

Although I was disappointed that I never heard from them, I now had a new purpose. Our farm. Our land. It was time to focus on a new life.

Despite being out in the country, far away from the crowds that drove me nuts, evidently, I still could cause problems. I noticed an issue with drainage and began to take Solomon out with a plow to make improvements. Our new farm neighbors complained. Apparently, it was a public thoroughfare and therefore off limits.

Joy continued to insist on my therapy sessions. Sometimes she would take me to out-patient therapy, trying to make a date of it. But invariably, the psychologists would give up. I overheard Dr. Doug Eckstein and his colleagues talking with Joy.

"Mrs. Lathrop. This may not be the right group for Gene."

"Why is that?"

They were hesitant to answer. I knew I tested their patience.

"He . . . he can be difficult."

"How so?" she asked, but already knew.

"He talks over the other patients. He monopolizes the sessions with his stories."

"As though he's the only patient?" she knew this routine well.

"Yes. Mrs. Lathrop. We've tried every possible form of therapeutic communication. But he just dominates each and every one."

"He is telling us what to do," another complained.

"Please, just try to work with him," she encouraged.

"Then you have to talk to him. Tell him to listen. Not just talk."

"I will. Sometimes, I can get through. But, please. Please. Let him continue," her voice sounded shrill. "It's all we have."

Just then, I came out of the therapy room.

"Gene. I swear, after an hour with you, my stomach is in knots. You're so keyed up. I feel like I need a Xanax myself," Dr. Erickson joked.

"Am I that bad?" I laughed to lighten the mood.

I knew my wife was at the end of her rope. My PTSD was also taking its toll on her. But I knew Joy was strong, despite her petite size. Luckily, she was independent too. She knew she had to be strong not to be dragged down with me. I had to find a way to help her hold her own. So sometimes, I encouraged her to go her own way. Spend time away from me. She was very involved in her work at the school. I knew it was good for her to have a break. That was the way it had to be, when living with someone with PTSD. Your spouse couldn't let themselves get sucked in. Joy knew that. And secretly, so did I.

Chapter 49

The farm was great. I loved riding Solomon. He knew just how much I could push him and when to fight back. Interesting enough, just like my wife. But I realized, that in order to help Joy survive, I still needed to have a getaway place. She needed her time and space and so did I. For me, that was the forests. Being the obsessive control freak that I was about money, I had a nest egg saved. I bought ten acres up in the mountains at Dayton, Washington. The property was near Walla Walla, where I was born.

Joy helped me make a hired hand's shelter in the barn. I had a bed, a stove, a make-shift table and a couple of chairs. When things got rough, I would take off with my horse and head for the mountains. Riding in the wilderness helped keep me sane. I also bought another typewriter. Writing and riding were the only things that kept my over-active mind going nuts.

I began to draft some poetry. It was healing to put my emotions into verse. I wrote about Vietnam. Getting shot down. What it was like to fly. Our missions. My Lai. All of it went on paper and down in verse. I called the collection, *The Dark Side of Heaven.*

Vietnam was history. A history that I took part in and that now threatened to destroy my life. But for now, I was in control of the PTSD. On most days, anyway. I still had the nightmares, but now not so often.

Society needed to understand what happened to so many good men. My cousin had become curator of the Penrose Library. I made an appointment to see him. My writings. My pilot's log book. My diary from Vietnam. They were part of history and should be archived.

Our meeting went well, or so I thought. Leroy was pleasant enough. He took a look at the poems. He even made some notes.

"Gene, this is interesting material. I'll visit with the head librarian to see if we can archive it."

"Leroy, I just wanted to keep these documents safe. What better place than a library?"

"I hear you, Gene. But Vietnam is still a touchy subject for some."

"Yeah. You could say that."

"It was a controversial war. Lots of societal consequences."

"Lots."

"We'll just see. Alright? I'll be in touch."

But they weren't. My own library. My own cousin was no different than the rest. Penrose didn't want the material. Another rejection. More and more, I could identify with the vagrant veterans on the street. The ones who had completely withdrawn from society. I was beginning to wonder if anyone even gave a damn. No one seemed to care about issues that needed attention. Was it just society and the times?

* * * * *

But again, when I was at my lowest low, Joy intervened. She came home from school armed with travel brochures. For history trips to the Deep South. I needed another distraction. Taking trips with my enticing wife seemed like just the right fix.

We both enjoyed history. It was something we could share. Our first trip was to Savannah, Georgia. The magnificent architecture of antebellum homes was spectacular. Far different than anything I had experienced. During this trip, for the first time in ages, I felt relaxed. We plotted out each leg of the trip, stopping at quaint cafes and quirky hotels. I refused to fly. So on most of them, we drove. To mark this new period in our life, Joy highlighted her hair blond. She was just ravishing.

Sitting on the veranda, overlooking a watershed, I held up my glass of Chablis for a toast. I couldn't drink reds due to the effects of tyramine on my MAO inhibitors.

"To the love of my life, Joy. Who has become my lifeline. My reason for being."

"Awww . . Gene. Thank you," she blushed.

"No. I mean it. You are the only one. The only one who has stuck by me. Through it all."

"I love you. You old coot."

"For better and indeed for the worst."

"Indeed. We've gotten through the worst."

"I couldn't have gotten through it without you."

Her lip started to tremble. She choked back tears. "I know, Gene. But I made a commitment to you. And I won't ever give up."

"I got you something. From the shops." I pulled out a gift bag. Her smile broadened with elation. "Open it."

She quickly removed the tissue paper to reveal an embroidered journal. "Gene, it's exquisite."

"I'm not the only one that should write. I know you have a lot to get out too." I reached over and took her hand. Taking it to my mouth, I gently kissed it. I didn't deserve such a generous, good woman. But I thanked my lucky stars that I had her.

During these long journeys, Joy would write down her feelings and journal. I knew this was important, in order to not pick up the PTSD herself. She later shared some of her writings with me. Often, she wrote about feelings of guilt in dealing with me. I knew that it was difficult to have the patience, understanding and emotional intelligence to cope with someone like me living with PTSD.

"Are you sure you're okay living with someone clapping with only one hand?" I once asked her.

"What do you mean?"

"What if one day I just completely unravel?"

"Do you feel you're unraveling?"

"Don't you?"

"Gene, I really did marry you for better or for worse."

I was overcome with emotion at her statement. I put my arms around to hug that petite bundle of strength. No words were needed. In my heart, I knew she hated what we were going through. As I held her tightly in my arms, I prayed she would never divorce or leave me. I was smart enough to realize that sometimes, many times, my outbursts made her want to.

"Joy, listen," I said whispering into her ear.

"Okay," she whispered back.

"Doves. Just like at the farm." We could hear the coo coo cooing of a couple of doves. "It's a male, calling his mate."

"Coo coo," she whispered and kissed my neck.

"Coo coo," I echoed back. I held her so tightly in my arms. Every time I heard the doves at the farm, I relaxed. I knew Joy understood better than anyone my love of nature.

Joy lived in a constant state of anxiety and nervousness, never knowing what I would do next. After an outburst, I would apologize profusely and feel tremendous guilt. Even though we both were writing, the incidents left scars. I knew she worried about my mental state. All the trips were very relaxing. We were great travel companions. When we would come home, I felt calm and relaxed, more like my old self. But inevitably, the PTSD would always come back rearing its ugly head.

Chapter 50

∞ Fall, 2000 ∞

During the summer, I again heard from a VMA-311 buddy. Pete was coaxing me to go to the squadron reunion. Joy was too. I really had absolutely no interest in sitting around with my ex-military buddies shooting the breeze about 'Nam. I was trying desperately to escape the torture of remembering it.

But Pete was relentless. After months, in a moment of weakness, I decided I would go. By myself. It was during the school year and Joy would be teaching.

"But Gene. That's a long way to drive by yourself."

"For Christ's sake, I ferried an A-4 9,000 miles across an ocean. I think I can manage a few thousand in a car."

"I just worry about you. That's all."

I might be mentally off, but I could at least drive. She knew she was treating me like a baby. I understood she was concerned. But the thought of miles alone, in total solace. Just the radio and the road. The break would do me good. And keep me away from the concerned neighbors.

Planning the trip gave me something to do. I got out all my maps and ordered more from AAA. For weeks, I mapped out which route I would take from Oregon, down through Idaho,

Wyoming and Colorado and then into the Deep South. The reunion was planned at Pensacola at the US Naval Air Station there. I hadn't been there since pilot training. One of the events was a tour of the National Museum of Naval Aviation.

Plotting the logistics on my maps, I figured it would take me about three to four long days of driving, depending on how many side trips I took. I planned every stop down to the last detail. I left out in my old pick-up truck early in the morning on a crisp day in October. Even before the sun was up. Thermos of coffee. Some sticky buns that Joy had made. My maps. And just me.

The loneliness of the highways and bi-ways was serenity. With my windows rolled down, aviators on, and my straw cowboy hat holding my hair down, I flipped the radio from one country station to another, from town to town. I used a pay phone to call Joy a couple of times a day, just to let her know I was okay.

But as fate would have it, my long awaited road trip was doomed. I heard the thump, thump, thump, thud on Highway 89 in northern California. Just past Black Butte, finally getting off the dreaded Interstate 5 on the way to Reno. My spare was in good shape. But as I checked the other tires, one seemed too risky on its threads. Kicking the old tire with my boot in frustration, I tried to think about what to do. Call Joy in defeat? Dag nab it.

Several hours later, Joy met me at a coffee house in Black Butte. I had hitched a ride back.

"Don't even say it," I warned shaking my finger at her.

"I wouldn't dream of it. So what is the plan?"

"A U-Haul tow hitch. I've already rented it. We'll tow the truck."

She knew better than to make me feel worse than I already did. I felt like a bloody fool.

"And the reunion? I take it that's off?"

"Hell no."

"Oh?" the surprise in her voice was obvious.

"Yep. I've booked us tickets. We're flying out of Eugene on American."

"But you hate flying. When you're not the pilot."

"Don't I know it."

"Gene, sometimes you are full of surprises."

"You wanted me to go, didn't you?"

"I wanted you to go because I thought it might be good to be around other people. Your fellow Marine pilots."

"That might also have PTSD?"

"The counselor said it would be good for you to talk about it. Around other folks who might have experienced the same thing."

* * * * *

I popped a double dose of Xanax before the plane took off. After being in the cramped cockpit of the A-4, you would think that the passenger cabin of a DC-10 would have felt huge. I pulled open my shirt collar and loosened my tie. I couldn't have felt more claustrophobic. My pulse was racing. I saw the pilots entering the cockpit. They couldn't have been more than twenty-six or twenty-seven. What the hell did they even know about flying?

As the tires came screeching to a halt on the tarmac at Pensacola, I wondered what I had gotten myself into. Marines. Oohrah. Gung ho. Hey diddle-diddle. But I had a responsibility to mentor other young pilots. That's what Erenfeld had said.

Pulling into the Holiday Inn, the anxiety which I felt on the tarmac, kicked into overdrive. Joy prattled on about the palm trees, the flamingos and the sunshine. I didn't even notice. What would I say to these people? My fellow scooter pilots. Would I even know them? I watched as several couples happily unloading their suitcases in the parking lot. There were some younger pilots in their flight suits. It was going to be a long weekend.

Chapter 51

J oy was enthralled with the Floridian culture and environment of the hotel. I couldn't have cared less, really. There
were young jet jockey pilots running around in their green
flight suits. Older veterans like me, in leisure clothes. The
testosterone in the lobby alone was palpable.

My eyes scanned the crowd for anyone I knew. We all
looked so much older. At least I had seen Pete in recent years.
Joy had the brochure of the weekend's events.

"Look, Gene. There's a tour to the new aviation museum at
NAS Pensacola. I'm sure you would like that."

"Yeah. Maybe so."

My stomach turned over. The hypnotic effects of the Xanax
were wearing off. I took out the pill container and took another
one. How could everyone be so happy? Didn't they understand
what was going on with those of us from 'Nam? It was like a
lightning bolt hit me. That was why I was there. I had to
enlighten these young pilots.

"Come on, Joy. Let's find our room. We've got mingling to
do."

I took a look at the schedule. Happy hour. Perfect. I needed
a drink. Maybe the other pilots would be more loosened up and
willing to listen.

"What should I wear to all these events, Gene? I'm a little bit
unsure."

"Baby, you always look great." I took her into my arms. "I'm so happy it worked out this way. Wear that little blue number. The one with the shorter pants."

"You mean the Capri pants?"

"Yes. You have gorgeous legs. You'll look amazing. The guys will all be jealous."

"Oh, Gene. Stop," she blushed.

We made our way down to the main lobby and into the "Ready Room." The "Ready Room" was a throwback to our pilot days, where pilots gathered to get the scoop and poop on their missions. Now it was jargon for our happy hour meet and greet sessions.

There was a large VMA-311 Tomcat logo blown up and hung over the make shift bar. It was serve and be served. I hadn't seen this much alcohol in years. As we entered, I finally saw a familiar face. Pete.

"I can't believe my eyes. It's the recluse. Gene Lathrop." He greeted me with a bear hug. "I'm so glad you came. I never thought you would."

"I'm full of surprises."

"And complete with the hat," he said referring to my cowboy hat.

"I'm never without it."

"Well, come on in. What can I get ya?" he motioned toward the bar.

I eyed the selection. "Maker's Mark. On the rocks."

Joy gave me a look. I knew she worried about the effects of alcohol with the meds. But I had been slipping secret shots for months.

"And for the lovely lady?" Pete asked.

"Um. I'll have a blush wine if you have it."

"Coming right up."

Pete served up our drinks. He seemed genuinely happy to see me there. He was wearing a VMA-311 polo shirt. Some khaki shorts. Top siders and of course his cigar. Just chewing on it.

"So how's life been treating ya?"

"Good." I answered. Again the look from Joy. "We bought a farm. Out near Sutherlin."

"Washington?"

"No. Oregon. Joy's still able to commute to teach in Rosenberg."

"Wonderful. You got livestock?"

"Some. Mainly my brilliant gelding. Solomon. I love riding."

"You don't say? I never knew you were a real cowboy."

"As real as they get, Pete. What about you?"

"I retired from insurance. I too got tired of the big city and bought a place up in Montana. We love it. It's at Whitefish."

"Good for you. There's nothing like the outdoors."

"That's for sure."

Joy and Pete's wife had begun a conversation of girl talk. It was good to see her engage with the other pilots' wives. Maybe I had been remiss in not involving her in the Marine veteran culture for support.

"Quite a lot of young pups here," I mentioned.

"Yeah. VMA-311 is still alive and kicking. Did ya know they've added the Harrier?"

"You don't say."

"Yeah. During the Gulf War. Circa '98.'"

"Hmmmm."

"Now that would be a trip to fly. Taking off vertically," he motioned with his arms.

"Yeah. Sure would," I took a sip of the welcome liquid relief. I wondered why I was here. All the 'oohrah' mentality of the 'gung-ho' macho Marines. It was so ubiquitous to the scene. I was having trouble relating to it. I hated crowds. I always did.

"Do you think any of the young pups even know what we went through?"

"Dunno," Pete answered in a nonchalant tone. "Maybe. But there's been more conflict since then. The Gulf war isn't any picnic."

"True. But it ain't nothing like Vietnam."

"Gene," Pete put his hand on my arm. "I know what you've been through. What's been bugging you. But go light, okay? Just go light. Enjoy being a hero for the pups."

I didn't like where Pete was going with his suggestions. Go light? Why shouldn't our younger pilots be warned of what a controversial war could warrant? The aftermath. I ignored him.

Throughout the remainder of the evening, I sat alone with Joy at a table out of the crowd. I was never good around lots of people. I wasn't sure what to make of Pete's guidance. I felt stifled. Wondering why I was even there.

The next morning was a breakfast. Joy and I joined the group. She was trying to be so encouraging. I was just going through the motions wondering when it would end. Thank God for benzos. I popped another pill.

At this event, there were more wives present. We were seated at a table with two or three older pilots and their wives. They too had been in Vietnam. I saw an opportunity and took it.

"That scooter. She was a sweet ride," one of them offered.

"Definitely. Sweet."

"The way she'd JATO off the SATS runway."

"Yah, there's no jet jockey here who understands scraping a hook, sparks flying on a SATS." There was laughter around the table.

"So what years were you guys there?" I managed to ask.

"Sixty-six and sixty-seven," one pilot answered.

"Sixty-five for me," replied another.

"I was there during TET. Sixty-eight and sixty-nine."

"You don't say? Heard there was some bad stuff during that time."

"You could say that for sure. Heard of My Lai?"

"A little. In the news. Why?"

I leaned in close to the table. "Because. I was there. Part of it. It's a huge government cover-up," I offered, taking a slug of my drink. Their faces looked dumbfounded. Which was all the permission I needed to enlighten them.

"Yeah. From Colin Powell on down. It's a damned cover-up. I was offered a million from Connie Chung to talk about it."

"What do you mean? The whole Calley thing?"

"Yeah. That's over," offered one pilot. "It was all Calley and the Army."

"No. It wasn't," I was on a roll. "We were asked to cover it up. Napalm the evidence."

"What? You're not making sense," the pilot shook his head.

"Us Marines? You're nuts dude. Never happened," said another.

"That's just a bunch of chit," a mechanic smugged.

"No. I'm telling ya. It was all a cover-up. VMA-311 was charged with napalming the evidence. My log book proves it."

I saw Joy's expression fall. She knew I was off onto one of my tangents. I ignored her facial pleas to keep quiet and launched into one of my dissertations on the subject.

After a few moments, the other Marines and their wives made a polite excuse for leaving our table. Then it was just Joy and myself. Sitting there. Alone. No one approached.

"Gene. We were having a good time," Joy beseeched. "Why did you have to go off on My Lai for gosh sakes?"

"Because it's a part of who we are. VMA-311. We were responsible. People should know."

Joy put down her drink. "Maybe people don't want to know, Gene. Maybe they don't' want to remember?"

She got up and strode off. I assume she went back to the room. I just sat there. I didn't want to admit she was right.

Here was a room full of pilots. Pilots who had undergone the same training I had. The same challenges. Honor, courage, commitment. Semper Fi. Seize the day. That was all I was trying to do. As a veteran, wasn't that my duty? To inform our replacements? Let our junior officers in on what was really going on?

Pete noticed that I was sitting alone. "Hey Marine. What's cooking?"

"They didn't want to talk about any of it." I hung my head.

"Any of what, Gene?"

"My Lai. The cover-up. Vietnam for fuck's sake."

At first Pete sat silently. "Gene, this reunion is for good times. Remembering the scooter. The missions. Helping mentor our young pilots. A lot of us want to forget the bad shit about 'Nam. We just don't wanna go there."

I sat silently. Not able to even make eye contact with him. He just didn't get it. He was just another one of the 'oohrah gang.'

"Listen. The night is young. Take a break. There's a great banquet with a band planned. Let's just have fun. I'm sure Joy would enjoy a night of dinner and dancing."

I was outraged. Why in the hell didn't anyone care? It had been proven. I had it in my log. My Lai. The mission that was responsible for fucking me up. Why didn't anyone give a shit? This whole event was nothing more than a pretentious spectacle. I wanted nothing more to do with it.

I got up from the table and strode off into the lobby.

"Gene, wait," Pete pleaded.

"I've had enough. Seen enough," I said punching the buttons on the elevator. I wanted to get the hell outta there. Too many people. I loosened the buttons on my polo shirt. My pulse was racing.

"Gene. Don't go. Just relax. They'll forget about that little drama. Calm down. Let's just have a good time," he pleaded.

I said nothing. I just wanted to pack and go home. Joy was so disappointed. But that is exactly what I did.

Chapter 52

∞ 2004 ∞

Pensacola was my first and last VMA-311 reunion. Don't get me wrong, it is a nice gathering. Maybe it works for some veterans. But I had no time for people who just didn't understand Vietnam. My experiences there were eroding the rest of my life. And seemingly, no one cared. No one except Joy.

After the reunion debacle, I spent more and more time in the woods. I moved Solomon from the farm out to the cabin. I knew Joy was worried about me. But I was determined to find a voice. Someone who would listen. It was my duty. If people understood, then maybe there would be answers to prevent more men from becoming mentally disabled like me with PTSD.

From the millennial year, I continued my treatments and counseling for PTSD at the VA. Now at Rosenberg. I was still taking a cocktail of drugs. Nardil. Xanax. Buspar. God knows what all those drugs did to my mind.

Besides taking trips with Joy and spending time at the cabin, my only other solace was spending time with my grandchildren on our farm in Sutherlin. Often times, I would take them to the small park in town. They seemed to possess a happiness that eluded me for the most part. So the afternoons I spent pushing them on swings, playing four square and supervising monkey bar madness were a relief. Until one particular afternoon.

On a gorgeous fall day, they innocently shattered that bliss. We had just finished dizzying our heads on the whirly wheel. Joy was with us and snapped a photo with them in my arms. Anna and Adam were snuggled in close. The smile on my face was genuine. I loved kids and felt lucky that after all the hell I had caused their mother, while she was in her teens, she had a big enough heart to let me spend time with them.

"Just one more photo," Joy pleaded. "You all look great."

"Then, ice cream." I suggested.

"I scream. You scream. We all scream for ice cream," they cheered.

Adam looked up at me. "Do you really scream, Papaw?"

"What do you mean?"

"Mom says that sometimes you scream at people. And scare them. That's why you all moved out to the farm. So you could scream at the animals. Not the neighbors."

"Yeah, Papaw. Are you crazy?"

I took them off my lap and stood them in front of me eye to eye. I took off my aviators so they could see my eyes.

"Look into my eyes. Do I look crazy to you?" I made the most intense, contorted face I could.

They erupted into laughter. "Only when you look like that. That's a crazy man look," they squealed with delight.

"Ooogahhhh boooogahhhh," I raise my arms and twizzled my fingers.

"Papaw. You are so funny."

"Papaw is funny. But not crazy."

I reached out my arms wide for another hug. They responded and I held them tight. I wasn't crazy. Not that I knew. Nor would I ever admit. Joy never said a word.

* * * * *

During that spring, I got a phone call that changed everything. It was a professor type, from Texas Tech University in a town called Lubbock, Texas.

"Hello?"

"Is this Robert Lathrop? Captain Robert Lathrop retired from the U.S. Marine Corps?" a curious male voice asked.

"That depends on who wants to know," I smirked.

"This is Dr. Richard Verrone. I'm a researcher from Texas Tech."

"It's a good thing you clarified that. I ain't got no use for shrinks."

"No, no. I am a historian. I'm working on a collection of oral histories from veterans that served in Vietnam."

"You don't say. How'd you get my name?"

"I saw a copy of the article from the interview you gave Dayton Sun."

"Oh yeah? I didn't figure many people read it."

"I read it. It was good. But I felt in doing so, you might have much more to say on the subject."

I processed what he was saying. Was he for real? Finally, someone wanting to listen? I couldn't believe my luck.

"Captain Lathrop?"

"Yep. Still here."

"Good, sir. So what I was wanting to ask is if I might set up some times that we could talk over the phone? I would be recording the sessions of course."

"About my missions in Vietnam?"

"About anything relating to Vietnam that you would like to share. Would that be okay?"

"Yeah. I think that would be just fine."

He asked me to get a calendar and we booked some dates for the interview. I decided to keep this all to myself. No need to worry anyone. At last, after all these years, there was an outlet. I could hardly wait. Finally, there was one person in the world, besides Joy, that wanted to listen. A library. A respected university. A professor. Someone who would take me serious.

Chapter 53

I t was 5:00AM and I was pacing. I couldn't wait for Joy to get up and get ready for school. It was Monday and I had been like a skittish cat all weekend knowing what was going to happen at 8:30AM Pacific time. I popped another Xanax to help me relax. I poured over my notes that I had written over the weekend. Dates. Times. Places. Feelings.

I was sitting at the typewriter when Joy stumbled in at around six. "Writing again, Gene?"

"Good morning. I thought you'd never get up."

"I sleep as much as a can. With the noise."

"Sorry, Joy. I'm on a new project."

"That's nice, darling. Happy for you," she mumbled heading for the kitchen.

"I've already made the coffee. Should still be hot."

"Thank you, my love."

Now 6:00AM. Joy would be gone in an hour. She liked to get to the school by 7:30AM. Plenty of time. Plenty of time. I shuffled my papers and re-ordered the notes one more time. I had no idea what he was going to ask.

"Gene. Want some eggs?"

"Thanks, hon. Nah. Too busy. I'll eat something later."

Walking Joy to the car, I kissed her goodbye, almost dancing back to the house. Alone at last. And only about an hour to go!

My anxiety was running over when the phone didn't ring at 8:30AM. Nor 8:31AM. Nor 8:33AM. Geez it was 8:38AM. I was about to jump out of my skin. Drumming my fingers nervously on the desk, I glared at the phone daring it to ring. But nothing. Had another opportunity bitten the dust?

But alas, at 8:40AM, I heard the ring that changed every-thing. I lunged for the phone, answering after it had only rung once.

"Hello? Hellllooooo?"

"Captain Lathrop. Good morning. This is Richard Verrone."

"I thought you would . . . that phone would never ring."

"Very sorry about that. We had some technical issues in setting up the recorder. I will remind you that we will be recording this session as per our agreement that you signed."

"Yes, sir. I understand. Let's get started."

I head a few clicking noises on the phone. Praying we weren't disconnected. But then I heard his voice.

<Verrone> This is Dr. Richard Verrone. I'm conducting an oral history interview with Mr. Robert Lathrop. Today is May 17, 2004. It's approximately ten forty-one AM Central Standard Time. I'm in Lubbock, Texas in the Special Collections Library interview room on the campus of Texas Tech University and Mr. Lathrop is in Sutherlin, Oregon. Sir, why don't we begin with where you were born and when you were born and a little bit about your childhood?

<Me> Okay. I was born in Walla Walla, Washington on June 8, 1942, which happens to be the day of the Battle of Coral Sea, I think.

<Verrone> Yes, sir.

<Me> And I have a photographic memory and I started documenting things before I could talk. And in World War II, we didn't have anything. My dad worked. He worked as a Caterpillar parts man. He couldn't go to war because he was the last person there in the business. We couldn't get gas, so I

remember the war. Boy, I can remember the war. We lived between a B-24 Base and a fifteen thousand bed Army hospital, so I saw the worst effects of the war.

<Verrone> Now where was this again?

<Me> Walla Walla, Washington

<Verrone> Okay.

<Me> Southeastern Washington. We had a big B-24 base on one end of town and the bombers came over our house at about eight hundred feet. And then on the other end, we had a fifteen-thousand-bed Army hospital with the worst casualties you can imagine. And so before I was two years old or three years old and up till when I was about five, I saw the worst of World War II. And the first thing that I have a perfect image of and I could draw it, was that crash. It turns out to have been in September of 1944, when I was two years and two months old. We went out and there was this massive fire and we were parked in an old pickup with a cracked window and my mother was there with her red hair. And in front of us, was a '37 Chevy. Behind us was a 1939 or '40 Chrysler. And off looking toward the town was a fire as far as I could see going east or west. You could smell flesh burning. I have a perfect image of that with the odors and everything and what I saw was a B-17 burning eleven people to death. And when I have an image so bright, it means the anxiety was so high.

<Verrone> Right. You said it was an image, the B-17 had crashed and eleven people were burning?

<Me> Eleven people were burning to death in the B-17. The base was a B-24 base. But for whatever reason the plane that was coming in and crashed was a B-17. Interestingly, thirty, forty years later, I went back to the same spot without ever having been there, with my Dad. I didn't know how I did that, it was like an imprint is in my body.

<Verrone> Right.

I heard him cough. Did he believe me? Was he getting all this?

<Me> Anyway, so I saw the worst effects of World War II. I grew up in a little town called Dayton, and I grew up sort of like Tom Sawyer. We had an old farmhouse when I first lived there. It was so cold in the wintertime, that I stuffed the windows. I grew up outdoors running up and down creeks and hiking in the mountains and bicycling out in the country. By 1950, things got better and my dad had a nice business. He was a John Deere dealer, so we were quite well-to-do. And I lived at the edge of town, but I spent all my time in the mountains and the hills and along the creeks. And I went to high school at Dayton High School.

We talked for about two hours.

<Me> So basically, my life was outdoors in sports from the time I toddled across the street into the forest when I was two years old in Walla Walla and it's been that way always. But in a sense, either I was that way naturally and my personality was that way or it affected my personality. Because I was never comfortable around groups of people. I tended to say things and do things that would distance myself, never really being comfortable as an 'in' part of a group.

<Verrone> Right. Okay.

<Me> I'm an independent. I was comfortable as a fighter pilot.

Was I rambling? I wasn't sure. But it was like a hurricane unleashed. I talked and talked and talked. I think I wore him out on the first day.

I told him about my childhood. He asked about my education. How I became a pilot. We started talking about my crash and how it affected me in Vietnam.

<Me> When your burns heal, you don't get the skin back like it was before. Something that started happening, like when I would get mosquito bites and scratch, my skin would bleed. I have a farm and get scratched easily and things like that. So you

know, I never really recovered from that. The main thing I lost was - maybe that thing. The confidence that it won't happen to you was gone.

<Verrone> Right.

<Me> I mean. I knew it could happen to me because it already had.

<Verrone> Yes.

<Me> And I watched people change in combat from the cocky fighter pilot to the pained look in the eyes and the stress lines in the face after they got shot down. So it happened to other people besides me.

<Verrone> Right.

<Me> And so I went to Vietnam different than I was before that plane crash. And the one thing that was different was in the tiny cockpit of the A-4, I used to get claustrophobia at night and in the suit. And I didn't in other airplanes, so in a lot of planes I felt terror and I had no idea why.

<Verrone> Right.

<Me> If it was on night missions, it didn't justify it.

<Verrone> Right. Right.

<Me> I was not afraid in combat, but I was afraid in the airplane sometimes for no reason at all.

<Verrone> Yes, sir. Why don't we take a break?

I was sure I had worn him out now. Was he going to call back? It's a good thing we were about to break. I had forgotten that Joy was going to be home early. I quickly ended the call and sat down the receiver just as she was walking in the door.

Chapter 54

I n my second and final interview with Verrone, I decided to tell all. There was a lot of stuff I knew about from my research that had nothing to do with Vietnam.

<Verrone> This is Dr. Richard Verrone. I'm continuing my oral history interview with Mr. Robert Lathrop. Today is May 18, 2004. I'm again in Lubbock, Texas and Mr. Lathrop is again in Sutherlin, Oregon. Sir, let's pick up where we were yesterday. We had talked about the end of your training, you're getting shipped to Vietnam. And some of your missions.

<Me> I worked as an intelligence officer for my desk duty when not flying.

<Verrone> Did that make your job in Vietnam more difficult or easier?

<Me>I would just assume after a while, you know, I was pretty much numb to anything. I could read anything or hear anything and I had no emotion and that's something that happens I think to everybody.

<Verrone> Right.

<Me> I think you become overwhelmed and you just have to accept something and deal with it later.

<Verrone> Right.

<Me> So you can see the worst things ever. You got to put it out of your mind and go fly another mission.

<Verrone> How did you deal with death?

\<Me\> I didn't deal with it.

\<Verrone\> I mean, the idea of you being shot down or your fellow pilots being shot down, or knowing what you were doing on the ground?

\<Me\> I didn't think about it.

\<Verrone\> Okay.

\<Me\> Well, I had to think about it when it happened, but I'll tell you how they did it. We had planes take off and get shot down; we didn't get the opportunity to deal with it unless we were wingmen or the duty officer because what would happen is that the plane wouldn't come back. Okay, it would still be listed on the board, then there'd be a telephone call.

\<Verrone\> Right.

\<Me\> The duty officer would get up and erase the name and they'd go in and remove the guy's personal possessions and go through them and that's all we did and that's the way it was dealt with. You couldn't deal with it, you simply didn't deal with it and you shut that off and dealt with it later, which is one reason people started getting screwed up years later when this stuff starts coming out. Because what happens is you bury this and you become numb. Well, when you come back to society, you're still numb. You can't hold all that in. I see it in my family. I have an uncle from World War II, he never talked about the war, but as he got older and didn't have the strength, that's all he talked about. And it takes energy to hold that in.

\<Verrone\> Yes.

\<Me\> And you have the conditioned responses of combat. Battle fatigue and PTSD cause a change in personality. Your adrenaline goes sky high and so your tendency is to run away or if you're the type of person that charges and attacks, you'll destroy the enemy. If you run away, you're probably going to become a casualty. Then it comes back to normal. In Vietnam, you didn't have time to come back to normal. It went up and it'd come a little down to normal. Then you'd be back up pretty soon. You're up all the time and you're highly alert and the fight or flight syndrome reverses. You don't get afraid anymore, you get mad and if you stay that way long enough, it's irreversible. You get mad and you stay mad and you stay aggressive, so when you come back to society, you don't get afraid anymore, when somebody confronts you, you're going to turn on them and attack them. Okay, it depended on your value system. A lot of people came back and fought that with drugs. A lot of people ended up in the pen and a lot of people ended up like myself holding it in and ended up with PTSD.

<Verrone> Right.

<Me> Because ultimately, as you get older, you don't have the energy to hold it in and it starts coming out anyway. And that's how a lot of people would start having . . . I started by having nightmares. Okay? And I started by having a job where I could go all the time. I was always happy leaving, but when I got someplace to work in forestry, I felt uneasy. I always wanted to go to somewhere else because you're always trying to run to someplace that stress isn't. So for a long time after the war, you saw people that'd hitchhike or something on the road. You'd ask where they came from? Were you going there? Well, they're running from themselves and I did the same thing in my job. I would go . . . I'd just feel great leaving town. Going out to work in the forests, but two or three days working someplace, that stress would still be with me, and so I just started running and becoming a workaholic. But what was happening is, it was getting worse all the time. I went into my first period of depression about a year after...not even a year, six months after I was released from active duty and I went to Vietnam right then, so it was about close to a year and three quarters when I got back. And so about three or four months after I got out, I went into depression and didn't even know what it was. It lasted a couple of days and then went away, but it got to be longer and longer and longer.

<Verrone> Right. Was there a mission, or task that you were ever asked to do that changed things? How you thought about the war?

This was it. It was time to let it all hang out. I was ready to get My Lai off my chest.

<Me> Besides Khe Sanh, which I have written a poem about. There was one.

<Verrone> Go on.

<Me> My missions were pretty routine. In and out. Drop the ordnance on the targets and get out. And because I never attacked intact, you know, undamaged villages, my wingman and I had never seen anything like this mission. The village looked intact, so we took a good look at it. During my first run, I got aborted and so I rolled inverted about six hundred feet and looked down into the streets. It was a great big village with little huts and you could see the grey walls of bunkers, but you couldn't see any people. It was a preplanned antipersonnel attack; that was the nature of the ordnance, but in the shadows of the evening, you couldn't really see people and there was something wrong with the mission. I mean nothing matched in it. Like, we were told we were attacking an enemy battalion with no ground fire and then they aborted us on the first run. You don't ever do that when there's friendly . . . you only do that when there's friendly forces in the area and the friendly forces were mostly about fifteen hundred meters . . . but anyway, I remembered the mission because it was just outside our landing pattern. And I never saw an intact village, but we took it out. It was first napalmed and the flames, they were so high that my last run I actually flew through them, they were lapping around the cockpit. Then they totally covered the village with the delayed fuse bombs, which penetrated bunkers underneath and blasted the bunkers apart, carrying the fire down.

<Verrone> I'm sorry, what was the purpose of this mission?

<Me> The purpose of the mission I presume was to take the witnesses off the map. I just talked to a guy, the first person I've ever known that knew about it. He said they were watching it from the American Division Headquarters because they could see it from our base. So, it was a cover-up.

<Verrone> Okay.

<Me> It was the final decision.

<Verrone> So it was an effort to get the people who could prosecute Calley and . . . who?

<Me> To get the witnesses gone apparently, and I'm not too sure it is as it appears as I say it, as a preplanned antipersonnel attack.

<Verrone> Right.

<Me> And I saw both villages destroyed because of the massive fire, but there was something wrong with the mission, too. Why, when we showed up so slowly, didn't everybody run out? But the way the attack was, it was an attack on people in underground bunkers and we wouldn't have seen them.

<Verrone> Right.

<Me> But it was a preplanned antipersonnel attack and the reason that it was preplanned is that it was atypical ordnance. You had surface ordnance in the first mission, then subsurface ordnance on the second; you'd do that. And it wasn't done by anybody in the Army, it was two Marines A-4Es, two Air Force Phantoms and an Air Controller from the Air Force, so there was no Army involved. And years later when General Powell was running for president, I heard people calling in from the Americal Division saying he was the operations officer that orchestrated it.

<Verrone> Was he?

<Me> Huh?

<Verrone> Was he?

<Me> Apparently. However, however . . .

<Verrone> Okay.

<Me> I have the dates October 8 and October 9. I've got tactical maps to go with my . . . see, I have the coordinates in my flight log book.

<Verrone> Right.

<Me> Bravo 5 715 789. Those are the map coordinates and I also got the date and time within fifteen minutes and I was the intelligence officer. I know the casualties. I talked to other people and at first, I thought, you know, here, I have unique knowledge. As far as I know, everybody that knew about that mission was on it in the Marine Corps and the Air Force was dead within a year. By 1970.

<Verrone> Why weren't you killed?

<Me> Well, I kept a diary.

<Verrone> Okay.

<Me> Every plane from the 28th of October '68 till the 15th of February '69, every single plane I was scheduled to be flying on ended up with fuel problems. Two of them I didn't take, one disappeared, the other crashed. The rest of the time, I made emergency landings.

<Verrone> Really?

<Me> Yeah. However, there is another . . . I mean, that doesn't make any sense. Planes don't have fuel problems, but it happened and they were all fueled at different places. I can't prove anything except the probability of everybody dying suddenly and unexpectedly alone in accidents, is it right, except there might be a secondary cause. The stress of being involved is so great; I think it could kill people at the time.

<Verrone> Right.

<Me> The people I knew that all died, died in ways that I would expect under extreme stress; drunks and car wrecks, a heart attack. The two that disappeared don't compute. It was the only two people I ever knew that disappeared in broad daylight. They were the two involved in that.

<Verrone> How many people?

\<Me\> Pardon.

\<Verrone\> How many people in total were involved that you know of?

\<Me\> I'm talking about only the people I know.

\<Verrone\> Okay.

\<Me\> I know, and that might not be significant because you can have more than one cause. The stress of being involved in something like this . . . as I say, I blocked my memories of it. I mean, I can't describe to you what it's like to be the real person responsible for the My Lai massacre because Calley didn't do much, but we did. So when you're talking about the My Lai massacre, most of the people were killed by us and it had to be that way and the only way it could not be is if somebody else killed them and we covered them up, covered it up.

\<Verrone\> Right.

\<Me\> But I've never run into anybody that said that. I have run into other people, and I also sought an appraisal for my historical file and I ran into the same exact statement from other people and they didn't say that it was populated and they did kill them, and one was a Marine. There was another Marine, made a statement and I was calling, getting appraisals and the appraiser had appraised his documents saying exactly the same thing I said. And he was on a patrol up on the hill. Well, that's the hill we bombed. After we hit My Lai IV, we had surface ordnance; we attacked the hill with both utilities. Well, we had the hills, not the enemy and I think they were just dumping our ordnance.

\<Verrone\> But dumping it on friendlies?

\<Me\> I don't know. I think the controller was just dumping our ordnance somewhere because we had surface ordnance and when they brought the two Phantoms in, they used delayed fused ordnance, which penetrated the bunkers.

\<Verrone\> Right.

\<Me\> And all we'd done is blown fire all over ourselves.

\<Verrone\> Do you think that they offered you the Distinguished Flying Cross so you'd keep quiet?

\<Me\> I just know it's a pattern, they offered the DFC to the helicopter pilot in the first attack to make him quiet. Everything that happened the first time happened the second time.

\<Verrone\> Right.

\<Me\> Okay, and it just fit the pattern.

\<Verrone\> Has anybody in the last...well, what kind of contact have you had with people about this in the last few years?

\<Me\> I was offered a million dollars for an interview. Connie Chung tried to interview me; it was blocked.

\<Verrone\> Who blocked it?

\<Me\> I don't know. I'll tell you that things have happened that tell me that they don't compute. Especially when I contacted Calley's attorney. Here's the ethics of the press, the 1970s court-martial. You cannot sue the press for what they won't write. Even if what they do write is no longer true. So they can start writing a story, get more evidence and they don't have to write it. The second thing is that no one who was released from active duty or discharged was reachable by the Army for the court-martial. And that's because the Army doesn't have the right of the International Tribunal in . . . where is it, Europe somewhere?

\<Verrone\> In The Hague.

\<Me\> The Hague - to call people back who are out of the Army. The Army can't do that. Third one is the most important. After World War II, not everyone tried as a war criminal was tried at the Nuremburg trials. Some were tried by the United States Army and they were given the right of appeal before the Supreme Court and one general did so, setting the precedent for Calley to do so. And so I was asked to contact him and tell him about the attack . . . and I sent a letter to him and I always sent more than one letter to document it and I have a file. He didn't reply, but I'm not sure my letter has ever gotten through to him because the one thing is, if you brought the My Lai thing up, you bring a whole lot more up.

\<Verrone\> Yes sir.

\<Me\> That's just what happened at My Lai. Because when I did my research, the first thing I looked at was not what Hersh wrote or books; I looked at the Federal Register. I looked at what Congress said and what Congress said was that there were five villages. That was right in the Federal Register and so really what I think is if they would've expanded the area of search, they'd found more villages until they'd have been all over Vietnam and would've found hundreds of them. And the reason is the enemy used their own people as shields.

\<Verrone\> Right.

\<Me\> But I kept a diary in Vietnam and that diary's in my historical file and you know what in that diary is significant?

\<Verrone\> What's that?

\<Me\> The worst things I write have shown no emotion. There is no emotion in that diary whatsoever. Anything, what you eat is described the same as the worst. The worst situations there ever was is when people were shot down and they were killed.

\<Verrone\> Right.

\<Me\> They would talk to you on the radio as they're getting killed, call in artillery on themselves. The other thing is, do you remember the movie, Platoon?

\<Verrone\> Yes.

\<Me\> What was the last scene in Platoon, they call an air strike in on themselves.

\<Verrone\> Yes.

\<Me\> Do you ever wonder what a pilot thinks when they say, 'Hit the white smoke' and all the radios go dead? You know, well, we didn't know they did that. All we knew, a bunch of friendlies got killed and they did. They did call in air strikes on themselves because it was better to do that than to get captured. They didn't capture people really. So, we were left with a lot of questions and a lot of the questions that other people had were answered for me by intelligence reports. But I had no way to communicate that to anybody but my commanding officer who told me what I could and couldn't do.

<Verrone> What made you change your mind and come out with all of this and to start writing letters and start talking about it?

<Me> Well, I blocked the war out, and then I lost my job and went to the treatment center and they teach . . . I watch people . . . see, a lot of people there, they put people together alike. Everybody there was like me, well employed and everything and had done well and all of us, we're all divorced, we can't remember the war. What they do is they get you angry so that you'll deal with the war. And then they teach you ways to deal with the anger and one way they teach you is to write, to write down what you think. And I do, I write it down quite often and I throw it away. It's an expenditure manager. The first time I wrote about My Lai, it was a huge release, but it didn't stay and the reason it wasn't because of me, it was because of what kept showing up in the press. Once I saw it in the press, it all came back. So I started responding to the press telling them to shut up. And it took about four letters and then the anger would go away, but I never got over the flashbacks of My Lai. And one reason I think, is because My Lai was a war crime. When Colin Powell ran for president, I heard so many people call in trying to turn him in and I could not believe it. And when we get in PTSD groups, or people from the My Lai incident talk, it is irrational today. I just simply don't think you can call an American a war criminal. And I think the same thing's going to happen to those people in Iraq that are treated that way. You can't accept the world opinions and make us like somebody that ran a death camp was. I mean, it took me ten years from the time I remembered My Lai until I realized it really happened. I

mean, I can remember it, but it took me ten years before and this . . . we're talking 1997.

<Verrone> Yes sir.

I finished up the interview with Dr. Verrone after another lengthy phone session. Looking back on it, I know at some point he must have thought I was just a rambling idiot. Playing it back in my head, I think maybe I was. The way he kept just saying "Right. Right. Right." It bothered me.

The interview was completed without me being heavily medicated. I just explained what was in my head and on my heart. But I was glad I did it. Glad to have gotten it out. Finally, someone who actually allowed me to talk about Vietnam. Still, I felt guilty keeping it from Joy.

Chapter 55

A few months after giving the interview, I contacted Dr. Verrone by phone. I wanted my writings, my poems and such to be a part of the archive. Maybe it would give my story more credibility. I went to the local copy shop in Sutherlin and made Xeroxes of my many years of typing. My experiences in Vietnam. I also sent the pen and ink drawings that a friend completed for me during my treatments at the VA. Still spending many nights at the typewriter, the interview had given me hope and a purpose to continue to record my experiences into a manuscript.

Finally, my life seemed to be coming together. Joy had decorated our home in Sutherlin divinely. It was filled with antique relics and knick-knacks in which we both found meaning. Old bottles and kitchen utensils. Canisters of products from another time. We both had an appreciation of history and happier times. I found a channel for my writing and submitted my manuscript to the archive at Texas Tech. Maybe in the future, one my grandchildren would read my materials.

One day driving back from the cabin to our farm, peace was shattered. Earlier that morning, while riding Solomon, I felt dizzy. At first I thought it was the humidity and heat. But I must have lost consciousness and fell out of my saddle onto the pasture grass. When I awoke, Solomon was protectively standing over me.

I dusted myself off, shaking my head to clear it. Must have been some kind of heat exhaustion or vertigo. Or so I thought. Joy was expecting me back for dinner. I remounted Solomon and cantered back to the barn. Once he was curried and groomed, I put up my saddle. Getting into my old pickup, I headed for Sutherlin.

* * * * *

The next thing you know, I woke up in tied down with all fours in the Emergency Department. The fluorescent lights and white tiles were all I could see.

"Where am I?" I screamed.

Rattling the stretcher I tried to shake loose the restraints. What the hell? I looked down and could see through blurry eyes that my wrists and feet were tied down tight.

"Where's the person in charge? Who runs this prison? Get me the fuck outta here." But no one seemed to be listening. No matter how loud I shouted. Someone in a pair of scrubs came and pulled the curtain around me and closed the door.

I was confused. Where was I? What the hell had happened? I struggled again with the restraints until I gave out. I was drifting in and out of stupor. Then a man in green scrubs was undoing my pants. I felt a jab in my left leg. They were medicating me. No. God no. My head felt like a weight was attached.

Sometime later, I was coming out of it again. Then I saw a face I knew. Joy.

"Joy. What are you doing here? You have to get out, before they tie you up too. Get out!"

"Gene. Listen. You are in the hospital. Not being held captive. The ER doctor called me. You passed out while driving back from the cabin. Your truck was overturned on Old Highway twelve."

She had tears in her eyes and her hands were shaking as she bent to kiss me. I had a wreck? But how? I passed out?

"What's going on. They have me tied down like an animal."

"It was for your own good. They had to sedate you to even run any tests."

"What tests? I didn't consent to anything."

"They thought you might have been having a heart attack or stroke, Gene. They didn't need your consent."

"That's bullshit. I know my rights. How dare anyone treat me when I haven't given them permission. This is a conspiracy."

"No, Gene. It isn't. It's your heart. It went into a dangerous pattern. It took a couple of shocks for them to convert you out of it. That's probably why you passed out."

"And you let them do this to me?"

"No. Gene. The doctor did what he had to do to save your life," Joy was crying while talking. "Just shut up, you big buffoon. You could have died."

"But I didn't. Maybe God's not ready for Gene Lathrop!"

Joy put her hands in mine. I felt guilty that I yelled at her. But damn it, I was mad. No one had any right to tie me down or hold me here.

"Take these restraints off, Joy. Now."

"I have to check with the doctor."

"No. God damn it, Joy. Get 'em off."

"Gene. Please. Try to cooperate. You are losing control."

"I'm not losing anything. I know exactly what I am doing. Go get the doctor."

"Alright. Alright. Just calm down."

In a few minutes Joy returned with a doctor who looked all of twenty.

"I'm Dr. Samuelson."

"How old are you? I'm a Vietnam veteran. I'm a God damned fighter pilot. Let me out of these barbaric ties."

"Mr. Lathrop," he began.

"Captain Lathrop. Captain Robert Gene Lathrop. U.S. Marine Corps. VMA-311. I demand to be let go."

"Mr. err . . . Captain Lathrop. Do I have your commitment to cooperate with treatment? We're very worried about your heart."

"Have I had a heart attack?"

"Well, no sir."

"Then get these mother fucking restraints off of me."

"Sir. If you can calm down."

I could calm down. I would calm down. If for no other reason than to get the restraints off. I quit wrestling against the stretcher and remained still.

"Thank you sir. You've had a rapid heart rhythm called atrial fibrillation with rapid ventricular response."

"And so," I said glaring at the nurse who had now removed the blue foam cuffs holding my legs.

"And so, when that rhythm occurs, your heart is beating so fast that blood doesn't get up to your brain. That was why you passed out."

"So what're you gonna do about it?" I queried.

"We used an electrical shock to your heart to cardiovert it. We shocked you twice. And since then, your heart rate has been normal with a normal, even rhythm."

"Then let me go."

"You need to be admitted, Mr. I mean, Captain Lathrop. You need to be seen by a cardiologist and started on medications to prevent the rhythm from returning."

"Oh hell, no. I'm not staying in any hospital. Especially one that ties you down." All the restraints were off and I started to sit up.

"Gene. Please."

"Joy. Stay out of this. It's none of your damned business."

She burst into tears. I knew I had hurt her. But I had to be in control. No one was gonna tell me what to do. Not now. Not ever.

I ripped out my IV and blood began to run on the floor. I grabbed my boots and headed for the door.

"Captain Lathrop. Wait." I heard them all pleading.

"Gene. Please. Stop," cried Joy.

But I wasn't stopping. I never wanted to be confined to a hospital again. I reached for my pickup keys which were still in my pocket and made my way toward my truck in the parking lot. Turning the key, I burned rubber out of the parking lot and into the darkness.

* * * * *

Hours later, in the wee hours of the morning, I pulled into the driveway at the farm. I must have driven for hours. Determined to make it to the farm at Dayton, I got halfway there and realized what a dick I had been to Joy. Entering the living room, I was only wearing my undershirt, as I had used my plaid shirt they had cut off of me to tie a tourniquet around where the IV had been.

Joy was laying on the couch. She woke up when she heard the creak of the door. Without saying anything, she ran to me, reaching up and wrapping her delicate arms around my neck.

"I was so worried, Gene," she whimpered, burying her head into my chest. "You big stupid ogre. I thought I was gonna lose you."

"You're never gonna lose me. You're stuck with me. Crazy and all."

"Crazy and all." And that was all she said.

I loved her more in that moment than I can put into words. I knew she was worried. So was I. The heart was nothing to take lightly. A cardiac dysrhythmia they said. Some kinda risk for forming blood clots from fibrillation something or another.

I had a long time to think about it. Taking a few cardiac meds wouldn't be that big of a deal. At least I was off most of the tranquilizers and psych drugs thanks to Joy. I wasn't ready to die. Not yet. Being tied down brought out the worst in my PTSD. It was Vietnam. It was the fire. It was the tight cockpit of the A-4. It was hell.

Chapter 56

∞ June, 2012 ∞

B efore I left for the cabin yet again, I ran my fingers over the gold plate of my two Distinguished Flying Cross medals. I was a fighter pilot. I was a Vietnam veteran. I had PTSD. I had put my family through hell, but I had survived. I looked over at Joy asleep in our bed. My sweet Joy. The love of my life.

I passed by the hallway pictures of my two sons. The one who tried to understand me, Arthur and the one that I wished did, Michael. I looked at the wedding photos of my step daughter Lisa. She had been an elegant and pretty bride. So many good times with Joy's boy Scott. He was a son to me too. I looked at the family snapshots of my parents' fiftieth wedding anniversary. Everyone appeared happy in the photos. My sister Susan. Her husband. My Joy. I looked pensive. That was just when the PTSD was rearing its ugly head.

In my pseudo, makeshift office, I touched the rigid, black keys of my typewriter. Would anyone ever read what I wrote? Would anyone ever listen or hear the interview that I had given Texas Tech? My life, despite the craziness of the PTSD, was good. We had a splendid home. I had an escape place, my cabin. I had my horse, Solomon. I was a lucky man.

I knew Joy worried about my heart. Evidently, the tests showed that I had micro vessel disease. The circulation in my heart was poor. I wasn't in congestive heart failure, but my heart was sometimes starved for oxygen. The physicians believed it was because of the years of stress from the PTSD. The emotional nightmare had now messed up the physical. Eh, my bad luck, I guess.

Bending down, I kissed Joy on the forehead. "I love you, Joy. You are my lifeline." I touched her cheek as she slept. It was about 2:30 AM. I wanted to be at the cabin when the sun came up. It was my favorite time in the forest.

Driving up to the gate of the cabin, I could see the glistening of the dew still on the grass. I heard a pair of doves calling to each other in the early morning hours. I felt at peace back in the woods. I spent the next few days working the land, writing and riding my steed.

On June 13th, I headed to the barn for another ride at dawn. I could hear Solomon getting restless. He was ready for his morning groom and outing. I planned to take him up the side of the tallest hill on our place. Today I felt a calling to be as close to God as possible. I brushed my warrior and put the blanket on. I lifted the saddle onto his back and was just buckling it tight.

But I never made it to the hill. While I was saddling Solomon, my heart started racing. I tried doing the maneuver the doctors had taught me, bearing down and grunting. A valsalva. But it didn't work. All at once, I saw a bright light. And then, everything went black. I lost consciousness and lay in the barn, next to my magnificent Solomon. I heard him let out a huge, "neeeeiggggggghhhhhhh." That is the last thing I remember of this world.

One of my neighbors saw Solomon running back and forth along the fence line. He had his saddle on. But no rider. They found me down in the barn. They did CPR to the best of their abilities. But it was way too late. I was long since gone.

An hour later, a sheriff's vehicle drove up our driveway in Sutherlin. Joy answered the door. After a brief exchange of words, her face fell and she collapsed into the sheriff's arms. Her tears were inconsolable. God, I would miss her.

My son, Arthur went up to the cabin. I'm sure it must have been difficult for him. He cleaned everything out. My typewriter. Boxes of papers and letters. Buckets. Lead ropes. Tack. Packaging things into my old pickup. He hitched up the trailer, loaded up Solomon and drove a lonely six hours to bring my belongings back to our farm.

* * * * *

I could see an urn. Joy had honored my request to be cremated. An American flag folded into the traditional military triangle sat next to it alongside my medals and pilot's helmet. I saw my children. All of them, including Michael, going up one by one to the urn. Michael bent down and kissed it. I wanted to cry out that I loved him. I always loved him. But no one could hear me. I saw my sister, Susan. I saw my angelic Joy. I heard them singing Amazing Grace. Then six pall bearers walked alongside as Arthur carried my remains. Joy and our other children followed down the aisle of the church.

Marines escorted me to my final resting place. I was buried in a field, high atop a mountain in Touchet overlooking the valley. The last thing I can recall is hearing the loud blast of a twenty-one gun salute. I had served my country with honor. And I felt that, as I watched them give Joy the American flag. Just then a dove let out a loud "Coo coo." Joy lifted up her black veil and looked around toward the forests.

"Coo coo. Coo coo." Joy just smiled. I know she knew it was me. Would anyone besides Joy ever know my story?

Chapter 57

∞ May 2013 ∞

A bout a year after my death, the phone rang in Sutherlin. Joy had been suffering from multiple myeloma and was just home from the hospital. I hoped she knew how much I had God's ear begging for her to get well. Begging Jesus to bring her comfort and be free of pain.

"Hello. I am looking for Captain Robert Lathrop. May I speak with him please?"

"I'm sorry," Joy answered. "Gene passed away a while ago. In 2012."

"Oh, I am so sorry to hear that," the voice sounded disappointed.

"Can I ask who is calling? This is Joy, his wife."

"Mrs. Lathrop. This is Jeanette Vaughan. I am a writer and just finished reading your husband's manuscript."

"His what?"

"Yes mam. His hand typed manuscript is in The Vietnam Center and Archive at Texas Tech University."

"Where are you calling from? A university?"

"No, mam. I am a writer from north of Dallas, Texas."

"And where did you find this? In a museum?"

"Yes, mam. His manuscript and some other items are part of an oral history project for the archive. In Lubbock, Texas. Evidently the graduate students have now converted all the interviews and materials into a digital format. I downloaded it and just finished reading the whole thing."

"Well, I'll be."

"It is quite a piece of work. Have you read it?"

"I had no idea he ever finished anything."

"Oh, I see. Well, I would be glad to send you a copy."

"That would be lovely. But what is it that you wanted with Gene?"

"Honestly? I wanted to get permission to use some of the descriptions of his missions and his body of work for a book that I am working on. It's actually about a Navy pilot. But I think it will work. It's called *Solo Vietnam.*"

"I see. I'm sorry. I am still getting over Gene's death. And I have been sick myself."

"I hate to hear that. I know this must have caught you off guard."

"Yes. I mean, I had no idea that he had even completed a manuscript. And you found it at a university?"

"Yes, mam. Online at Texas Tech University. Do you know who owns the rights to his material?"

"I don't know. I guess I do."

"Well, I sure would appreciate it if you would give it some thought."

"I will. I will. I will have to get back with you. Thank you for calling."

"No. Thank you. And God bless your husband for putting his service and memories of Vietnam and the aftermath on paper. You're welcome to call my number after you have time to think about it."

Epilogue

∞ February 1991 ∞

I have an image. It has always been there. I can remember it before I could remember anything at all. It is of war and death.

In the winter of 1991, I had been visiting my parents, who remained in Walla Walla, and was driving with my father around looking at all the old Victorian houses that dated from the 1880s when Walla Walla was a jumping off point to the Idaho mines and the county seat of the rich farming country around it.

The image of the fire I had always had in the back of my mind had a directional quality to it that led me back to where I thought it was. I had driven to the place I thought it was after being released from the PTSD Treatment center in the VA Hospital in Tacoma, after having the image and the entire war flood back into my memory, where it stayed. I never knew where it was, in actuality and asked my father to drive me to that spot.

I took him to where I thought it had been, but he said I was wrong and we drove a quarter of a mile away, on a road that was in a wheat field and above the spot I had picked. Everything fit now. I could place the B-17, the flames of the crashed aircraft, across the level wheat field where the men were standing in their jackets and hats, shielding themselves against the heat. The experiences of life and adulthood had given words to all aspects of what I remembered as I looked to where the 1939 Chrysler was parked and the 1937 Gray Chevrolet.

The road was still gravel, as Walla Walla had not changed much. The place where the burning B-17 had been located was still a wheat field also. The smell of burning flesh and fuel I had been subjected to, more than I had ever desired during the war, had been the smell that I had been repulsed by at the age of twenty months. This is where it all began. I was afraid of fire before I knew what fire was. Those same images of fire back then haunted me until after the war. Vietnam was where I had lived with fire for fifteen months.

It was all gone. The career, the future plans that I made for myself, my wife and my children. I was lost.

During the years in and out of the VA hospitals, I met hundreds like myself and learned not only from the veterans of World War II, but from other Vietnam veterans, what life would be like. I was now understanding the adjustments that had to be made to live with the conditioned responses changed by the long-term effect of the stress of war. Previously known as shell shock and studied from before World War II, it now had a name. PTSD.

As I stood there, I contemplated my life; envisioning the present through eyes that would always be in 1968. Learning to live with the ups and downs, deliberately isolating myself from society, I yearned to exist ever more peacefully alone. Survival demanded continually adjusting my inappropriate reactions to the present challenges. More importantly, after finding the coordinates of My Lai in my flight log book, remembering the nature of the mission, I realized now that I would remain eternally at war.

LATHROP & VAUGHAN

Glossary

ARVN: Army of the Republic of Vietnam
ASRAT: airport surveillance radar used to detect positions of aircraft
bird: plane
black shoe: shipboard or 'surface' officers and senior enlisted members, due to the black footwear worn while in uniform
brown shoe: aviation community officers and senior enlisted members due to the dark brown footwear worn in uniform
bunker: protected area within living quarters; reinforced hole or tunnel
BuNo: identifying numbers assigned to individual naval aircraft
CAP: combat air patrol
Carqual: carrier qualifications; test for landing aircraft on carrier
chopper: slang term for helicopters flown by the US Army
C-130: large Air Force transport plan for troops and cargo
CO: commanding officer
Dash 1: the lead on a mission
Dash 2: the second plane in a two-or-more aircraft formation; the wingman
eye on the meatball: keeping an eye on the gyroscope of the airplane
DMZ: demilitarized zone
IFF: identification, friend or foe
GCA: ground controlled approach
G suit: anti-gravity suit
Gs: gravity forces
greenieboard: the rating scale posted for each carrier landing in the ready room
hawk circle: orbiting stack of aircraft waiting to land on the carrier
HC-1: squadron of helicopters
helo: slang term for helicopters flown by US Navy
hooch: living quarters for military personnel; tent or fixed facility
I Corps: South Vietnam was divided into four corps zones by the ARVN. I Corps was the northernmost region bordering North Vietnam
Jolly green: U.S. Air Force HH-53 Super Jolly green Giants were the primary search-and-rescue helicopter in Southeast Asia

KIA: killed in action
les bon temp roulles: let the good times roll
Lt: lieutenant
Lt. JG: lieutenant junior grade
LCDR: Lt. Commander
LSO: landing signal officer
MIA: missing in action
MiG: Russian fighter made by Mikoyan-Gurevich Design Bureau
MiGCAP: missions during Vietnam to take out enemy MiG fighters
miniboss: second in command aboard an aircraft carrier
Montagnard: primitive hill-dwelling people of Indo-China
NAS: naval air station
NVA: North Vietnamese Army
O club: officers' club
POW: prisoner of war
PTSD: post-traumatic stress disorder
qual: qualify
Quonset hut: metal structure for supplies or living quarters
SA: situational awareness; is the pilot aware of surrounding threats
SAM: surface to air missile
SDO: supply duty officer
SERE: survival, evasion, resistance and escape is a training program
  that provides U.S. military personnel with survival skills in evading
  capture using the military code of conduct
R and R: rest and recuperation
ready room: where pilots gather for brief and debrief
shrapnel: metal fragments from an exploding bomb or grenade
scooter: nickname for the A-4 Skyhawk jet
TET: the Vietnamese New Year
USO: United Service Organization a group which supports military
VC: the Viet Cong guerilla warfare
Vice: tactical radio channel

References

A-4 Skyhawk Association. http://a4skyhawk.org/content/vma-311 Accessed August 8, 2016.

David Anderson L., ed. *Facing My Lai: Moving Beyond the Massacre.* Lawrence, KS: University Press of Kansas. 1998.

Grant, Z. *Over the beach: the air war in Vietnam.* New York, NY: W.W. Norton and Company, 1986.

Gray S. *Rampant raider: an A-4 skyhawk pilot in Vietnam.* Annapolis, MD: Naval Institute Press, 2007.

Hersh, S. *My Lai 4: A Report on the Massacre and its Aftermath.* New York: Random House 1970.

Interview on CNN's Larry King Live. New York: U.S. Department of State. May 4, 2004. Archived from original January 10, 2007. https://web.archive.org/web/20070110175317/https://www.state.gov /secretary/former/powell/remarks/32160.htm

Klein R et all. Former American prisoners of war. Washington, DC: Office of the Assistant Secretary for Policy, Planning and Preparedness, US Dept. of Veterans Affairs, 2005.

Lathrop R. *The Dark Side of Heaven.* Blue Ridge, TX: AgeView Press, 2015.

Parry, R and Solomon, N. Behind Colin Powell's legend – My Lai. *Consortium for Independent Journalism,* July 22, 1996.

Sambito, W. *A history of marine attach squadron 311.* Washington, D.C: History and Museums Division Headquarters U.S. Marine Corps, 1978.

Verrone, R. Interview with Robert Lathrop, 18 May 2004, Robert Lathrop Collection, The Vietnam Center and Archive, Texas Tech University. Accessed March 10, 2013 http://www.vietnam.ttu.edu/virtualarchive/items.php?item=OH0360

Captain Robert "Gene" Lathrop, USMC, VMA-311 was a valiant pilot and decorated warrior during the Vietnam War from 1968 to 1969. He loved the A-4 Skyhawk lovingly called the "scooter." Lathrop returned from Vietnam with a hefty dose of PTSD. He lived the remainder of his life as a forester with the Bureau of Land Management. He desperately sought to understand the powerful images and memories of war that corrupted the remainder of his life. To try and make sense of it all, he penned a collection of poems, *The Dark Side of Heaven* and this memoir *Eternally at War*. His hope was that all who read his works can find comfort for their families in the aggressive treatment of PTSD.

Jeanette Vaughan is well-established as an award winning writer and storyteller. Not only is she published in the periodicals and professional journals of nursing, but also in the genre of historical fiction. Out on her sheep farm, she has written several novels and scripts. She is the mother of four children, including two Navy pilots. Jeanette has a deep-seated respect for the military and our Veterans. She lives in a Victorian farmhouse out in the pastures of northeast Texas with her sheep, chickens, donkeys and sheep dogs.

Follow me online here:

Blog: www.jeanettevaughan.com
Email: jeanettevaughan@ageviewpress.com
Facebook: www.facebook.com/AgeViewPress
Twitter: www.twitter.com/VaughanJeanette
Goodreads: www.goodreads.com/Jeanette_Vaughan

63071112R00200

Made in the USA
Charleston, SC
28 October 2016